INTRODUCTION TO PSYCHOLOGY
FOR MEDICAL STUDENTS

To Stephen Barton Hall
who was the inspiration behind the Course
on which this book is based

INTRODUCTION TO
Psychology
FOR MEDICAL STUDENTS

R. R. HETHERINGTON B.Sc. Ph.D. F.B.Ps.S.
Senior Lecturer in Clinical Psychology, University of Liverpool

D. H. MILLER M.B. Ch.B. D.P.M. D.C.H.
Consultant Psychiatrist, Clinical Lecturer, University of Liverpool

J. G. NEVILLE M.B. M.R.C.P. D.P.M. D.C.H.
Consultant Psychiatrist, Clinical Lecturer, University of Liverpool

WILLIAM HEINEMANN MEDICAL BOOKS LTD
LONDON

First published 1964

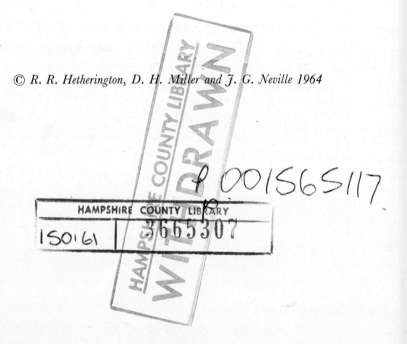
Printed and bound in Great Britain by
R. J. Acford Ltd., Chichester, Sussex

ACKNOWLEDGEMENTS

A book of this kind, based on a Course which has been developed and modified over a number of years, inevitably owes much to the many people who have given advice, counsel and encouragement from time to time.

We are particularly grateful to Dr. Stephen Barton Hall, who not only conceived the Course in the first place, but also read the book in manuscript. Mr. Geoffrey Leytham kindly read the typescript of the psychological chapters and made some valuable comments. Sir Cyril Burt has been good enough to provide the data for the last two tables in Chapter 5.

Many diagrams and charts have been specially prepared for the book, but the following material is copyright and has been reproduced by permission of the authors and publishers concerned.

Chapter 2

Fig. 1   British Journal of Psychology, 1908, 2. Fraser, J. " A new visual illusion of direction ".

Fig. 2   British Journal of Psychology, 1958, 49. Penrose, L. S. and Penrose, R. " Impossible objects: a special type of visula illusion".

Figs. 3 and 4   " Foundations of Psychology ". Boring, E. G., Langfeld, H. S. and Weld, H. P. 1948. London: Chapman & Hall. p. 300, Fig. 132. (*copyright: John Wiley & Sons Inc.*)

Fig. 6   As above. p. 220, Fig. 78.

Chapter 5

Fig. 1   " Measuring Intelligence ". Terman, L. M. and Merrill, M. A. 1937. London: Harrap. p. 37, Fig. 1.

Table 2 As above. p. 48, Table 12.

Chapter 7

Quotation on p. 70 is from " Textbook of Human Psychology ". McKeller, P. 1952. London: Routledge & Kegan Paul Ltd. pp. 39-40.

Chapter 9

Fig. 1   " Personality: A psychological interpretation ". Allport G. W. 1937. London: Constable. p. 91, Fig. 10. (*copyright Holt, Rinehart & Winston Inc.*)

Fig. 2   " The Structure of Personality ". Eysenck, H. J. 1960. London: Methuen. p. 369, Fig. 51.

Fig. 3   " Manual of the Maudsley Personality Inventory ". Eysenck, H. J. 1959. Univ. Lond. Press. p. 6, Fig. 2.

Chapter 11

Fig. 21 "Psychological Medicine".   Curran, D. and Partridge, M.
1955.   Edinburgh: Livingstone. p. 27, Figs. 1, 2 & 3.
Fig. 22 *The Practitioner*.   1956, 177.   Groen, J. and van der Valk,
J. M.   "Psychosomatic Aspects of Ulcerative Colitis".

The diagrams were drawn by Mr. Kydd and the photographic work
was done by Mr. Lee, both of Liverpool University.

Contents

PREFACE

As its title implies, this book has been written specifically for the undergraduate medical student. If it also proves useful to non-medical students and to medical graduates, this will be gratifying, although quite incidental.

The authors have had three years' experience of lecturing on normal psychology to undergraduate medical students in their third year at Liverpool. Most of the twenty-four lectures in the course have been given by one or other of the authors, and these have been followed by seminar discussions with small groups of students. It has therefore been possible to write this book with an intimate knowledge of the needs of medical students at this stage of their studies.

Care has been taken to relate the psychological data to the students' own medical studies. Material which has no direct bearing on medical theory and practice has been cursorily dealt with or omitted altogether. The book therefore does not pretend to give a balanced view of contemporary psychological theory, but has tried rather to give a clear exposition of those areas of the subject which are essential to a proper understanding of the psychological implications of medical practice.

Liverpool,   R. R. H.
September 1964   D. H. M.
                                                                      J. G. N.

Chapter 1

SCIENTIFIC PSYCHOLOGY AND ITS RELEVANCE TO MEDICINE

Scientific Psychology

Psychology is essentially concerned with " mental processes " just as physiology is concerned with " physical processes ". Its data are percepts, images, thoughts, feelings, desires and the like. Because of this, some have doubted whether such a field of study could ever become scientific, since the data concerned are not available for public inspection in the same way as nerve impulses, blood flow or glandular secretions.

While it is true that we cannot inspect or examine someone else's thoughts, percepts or feelings directly, we can observe and record what they do and what they say. Moreover it is open to every man to " introspect " or look inward, and thus to become aware of his own thoughts, feelings and desires. At the same time he can observe his own behaviour and speech, and so become aware of the kind of thoughts, feelings and desires he has when he behaves and speaks in certain ways. Thus when he observes someone else smile or laugh and hears him say: " I feel fine to-day ", he has some idea of what that person is probably feeling because he remembers how he felt when he behaved in similar ways in the past. Some writers, indeed, have suggested that it may not even be correct to argue by analogy in this way, but that we may well have some direct apprehension of the feelings of others. It is suggested, for example, that a small baby seems to sense and to respond to his mother's mood although he is clearly too young to argue by analogy. The same could be said of dogs, which also seem to respond to the moods of their human masters. If there is some direct apprehension of other people's inner experiences, we have no idea how it operates.

The difficulties inherent in guessing what other people are experiencing from observation of their outward behaviour, have led some psychologists to reject all introspective evidence of personal experience as being unscientific, and to concern themselves only with observing outward behaviour. Such psychologists belong to what is known as the " behaviourist " school. In its pure form such an approach was found to be too restrictive, and to ignore many important data necessary to the understanding of human behaviour. Most psychologists to-day have come to realise that the study of inner experiences is an important source of psychological knowledge. When a man says " I feel depressed " we are not only concerned with his " verbal behaviour ", the words he says; nor only with his physical behaviour, his facial expression, how he stands, walks or sits; but also with our own intuitive insight into how it *feels* to be depressed, gained from our own personal experience, however slight, of that condition. We can, of course, gain some knowledge of his thoughts because he can tell us what he is thinking: " I feel worthless, I've failed, the future is hopeless " and so on. Yet, as we shall see in later chapters, much thinking is non-verbal, and consists of visual, auditory and other kinds of imagery, so that verbal description of thinking is only a partial account of what is going on. To ignore the evidence of one's own introspections in evaluating other people's behaviour is to reject important sources of data.

This having been said, it must be stressed that psychology is a science, and must apply the same standards of exact, careful enquiry as pertain to other sciences. There must be the same empirical approach, and the same refusal to rely on armchair speculation or anecdotal evidence when studying inner experiences, as in the study of outward behaviour. Where possible, qualitative data must be quantified so that numerical comparisons can be made.

Scientific psychology is concerned primarily with the study of normal human experience and behaviour, and it can offer data about human abilities and thought-processes, about human emotions, needs and drives, and about the complex individual differences that go to make up human personality. We shall be concerned with much of these data in later chapters of the book.

Cognition, Affection and Conation

It is customary to classify both experience and behaviour into three categories, according to whether they are concerned with cognition, affection or conation.

Cognition is a term concerned with all types of behaviour or experience that lead to knowing. Thus behaviour such as seeing, listening, touching, and tasting, and the experiences to which these give rise; or experiences associated with thinking, imagining, and remembering; are all cognitive.

Affection is a term associated with emotional experience and behaviour, and feelings of pleasure or unpleasure.

Conation is a term associated with striving and effort, or experiences of craving, longing, desire or impulse.

These three terms, or their adjectives, cognitive, affective or conative will be used throughout the book.

Methods of Study

How can such intangible data as percepts, thoughts, feelings and desires be studied scientifically? As we have already observed, we can only study the external behaviour of others, obtaining intuitive insights into their experiences, by analogy with our own in similar circumstances. Naturally we have to depend heavily on other people's " verbal reports ". That is, we have to make a record of what they say they experience, what things look like and sound like to them, what in fact the world seems like to them. We have to depend on their telling us how they think, how they solve problems, and what they can remember. Data such as these can then be matched and compared, and the relevance of various environmental factors can be studied.

In studying any piece of behaviour, whether verbal or otherwise, we cannot rely on a single instance. In pre-scientific psychology it was a commonplace for people to quote as acceptable evidence a single instance of how a man behaved in a certain circumstance, and then to generalise from that, supposing that a universal rule of human behaviour had been discovered. Nowadays we have to be sure that we base our statements of how people behave on a study of a *representative sample* of the particular population or group of people we are concerned about. Such a representative sample would have to be a miniature of the whole population, having a similar proportion of people in it of various kinds, as existed in the population as a whole. This is sometimes achieved by taking a *random sample* of the population. Such a random sample could be taken from a school population by selecting every child whose birthday fell on a Monday. In this way a sample of roughly one-seventh of the school population would have been selected for study, and results from this could be held to apply with reasonable certainty to the school population as a whole. This could never be done if only one child from the school had been selected for study. On the other hand it is usually unnecessary and often impossible to test everyone in a school. Another way to sample a school population would be to choose a sample, taking care that it contained the same *proportion* of boys and girls of the sort of ages, intelligences and home backgrounds as existed in the school as a whole. The sample would in fact, need to be *matched* with the total population of the school with respect to as many of the variables as were considered to be relevant to the particular study being undertaken. Samples of this kind can be made as large or as small as is desired, although small samples less accurately represent the population from which they are drawn. A truly random sample, if large enough, is usually adequately matched with the population it represents.

Suppose we were interested in the effect of a certain drug on behaviour. The hypothesis to be tested might be that this drug acted as a sedative. In order to test this hypothesis, we should need to administer the prescribed dose to a group of people on a number of different occasions. We might then find that there were variations in its effect not only between the individuals in the group, but also between the various occasions on which the drug was administered. We should then need to study the various factors that might be contributing to these differences, such as time of day, body weight, relation to meals and so on. These would then have to be controlled, and altered one by one until the sedative effects were proved to be due to one or other or a combination of several of these variables. The phenomenon under study, namely the sedative properties of the drug is called the *dependent variable*. The factors which are controlled and altered one by one are known as the *independent variables*, because they are independent of the sedative properties of the drug.

The factors operating in producing the effects of drugs, or indeed the effects of treatment of any sort, are often most easily studied by matching a group of patients on whom the treatment is being tried, with a similar group of patients who are not being given the treatment. These two groups are made as similar as possible with respect to all the variables considered to be relevant such as age, diagnosis, sex and so on. The group not being given the treatment is known as the *control group*. The use of controls in this way has prevented many claims being advanced for the efficacy of new treatments, when it has been shown that " untreated " groups improve as fast as " treated " ones. This is particularly relevant to the treatment of neurotic illnesses which tend to remit spontaneously in any case, whether treated or not.

The development of the branch of mathematics known as *statistics* has given us many mathematical tools for assessing whether the effects of treatment are such as could have happened by chance, or whether the application of the treatment has made a real difference to the course of events. Suppose for example a man has an average of 3.7 migraine attacks a week over a period of six months. If he then takes a drug, and finds he now has an average of only 2.8 migraine attacks a week over the next six months, it is possible to calculate statistically whether this change is likely to have happened by chance variation, or whether the change is sufficiently large, relative to the chance variations up to date, to be unlikely to be due to random changes, and so can be attributed to the effects of the drug.

Interviewing has always been the basic method of enquiring into the problems of the patient. We ask him what the matter is, how long he has been ill, what his symptoms are and so on. This sort of enquiry can be systematised into formal *questionnaires* which ensure that nothing of importance has been omitted. On the other hand, if the enquiry is restricted to questionnaires there is a danger that the unexpected, but nevertheless important fact, has not been elicited because the appropriate question had been left unasked. In psychology, therefore, it is more usual to employ a *structured interview* which provides a systematic coverage of all the important topics, but leaves ample opportunity for the patient to volunteer information. When the area of the problem has been defined, more exact *test procedures* can be introduced. These may be tests for clearness of thinking, memory, acquired knowledge, or interests. These are usually well *standardised*: that is they have been tried out on large groups of people which constitute representative samples of the population as a whole, so that the patient's score on such a standardised test can be compared to that of the population as a whole, or to specified groups within that population. Nowadays it is increasingly becoming the practice to express a score on a test in such a way that the patient's performance is compared with the range of scores obtained from the general population, he can then be said to come in the top 5%, middle 50% or bottom 5% and so on. Tests may have to be specially chosen to examine hypotheses which have been advanced to explain the patient's behaviour. Suppose, for example, a patient exhibits a poor memory. This might be due to brain damage, or he might always have had a poor memory. The former hypothesis could be checked by giving specific tests known to be poorly performed when subjects have suffered brain damage. The latter hypothesis could be examined by giving an intelligence test, a low score on which would suggest that poor memory was part and parcel of an innate dullness. Such an intelligence test would, of course, have to be carefully selected only to include items which were known not to be much affected by brain damage.

Relevance of Psychology to Medicine

Much has been written in the last ten years or so, about the tendency of medical education to " dehumanize " the patient. (See Chapter 20.) Increased pre-occupation with laboratory sciences has tended to divert attention from the patient as a person, and to emphasise the mechanical workings of his body. The " psyche " has been ignored in favour of the " soma ". The pendulum is now firmly swinging the other way, and increased interest in psychosomatic medicine (see Chapter 11) and in such phenomena as the " placebo effect " of drugs (see Chapter 19) has focused medical interest once more on the psychological aspects of physical illness. Psychiatrists, of course, have necessarily had to be concerned with psychological factors, although even in psychiatry there has perhaps been an undue emphasis on physical and pharmacological treatments.

The relevance of psychology to medicine is therefore becoming increasingly evident, and is reflected in the increasing amount of time now being devoted to psychology in undergraduate medical curricula, where in some medical schools psychology is introduced at an early stage in the student's training. This relevance is obvious in the field of mental illness, and is becoming increasingly obvious in psychosomatic medicine. But it should also be realised that every physically ill patient, however mentally " normal " or " stable ", will have reacted psychologically to his physical symptoms and to the effects of his illness on his dependants, his work and his future prospects. Moreover, if he has had to be admitted to hospital, he may have produced further psychological reactions to the stresses inevitably associated with hospitalisation. If these psychological reactions have produced changes in the patient's emotional state, as they are very likely to do, then his physical condition may also have been affected, which in turn may have affected the course of his illness (see Chapters 10, 11 and 19). These " psychological reactions " are likely to occur in many, if not all normal people when they are ill, and can be expected as the normal course of events. Many puzzling features of the behaviour of people when they are physically ill, and the difficulties in communication with patients and their relatives, can only be understood if the total situation, psychological as well as physical, is taken into account. Why do some patients recover quickly and easily from an infection, and others take longer and only improve with many setbacks? Such differences cannot always be accounted for in terms of the physical differences of the patients. Psychological factors, when studied, may throw some light on to the problem. Some patients seem to have a " will to survive " and overcome massive physical handicaps and illnesses. Others succumb to relatively trivial injuries or infections. In primitive societies people will die for no other reason but that they have been told they will by the witch doctor. It is a common experience that under emotional stress people are often unable to take in what they are told, and it has to be repeated at intervals, or postponed to another occasion before a proper understanding occurs. Physical illness produces situations of emotional stress for the patient and the relatives, so that it is not surprising that difficulties of communication arise in the hospital ward or doctor's surgery. (See Chapter 20.)

Since the interaction of mind and body is now realised to be so intimate, it is short-sighted, or worse, to imagine that nursing or doctoring the body can be effectively performed without paying attention to the needs and satisfactions of the mind.

Chapter 2
PERCEIVING AND IMAGINING

A person cannot react appropriately to his environment unless he is able to perceive it. A doctor cannot treat his patient unless he can see him, hear him, and touch him. However, the process of perception is a complex one, heavily dependent on past experiences and future expectations as well as present stimulation. Thus each individual perceives his environment in his own particular way, and reacts to it as he perceives it. This may not be as others perceive it, nor may it be quite as it really is. It is thus clearly important for the doctor to know something of his own perceptual processes, if only to make him wary of relying uncritically on the evidence of his senses; and to make him realise that two people may genuinely and sincerely disagree about the nature of the environment they both share, and yet both be sane, honest and intelligent witnesses.

A Definition of Perception
" Perception " can be defined as the *"Awareness of objects, qualities or relations, which ensues directly upon the stimulation of sense organs "*.

We say that sensory processes are involved in order to distinguish perception from other psychological processes such as thinking, memory, feeling or willing which are not directly dependent on external sensory stimulation. At the same time, of course, perception is taken to include awareness arising from all the sensory modalities, so that we can say that we perceive pain, roughness, smoothness, hardness, and softness, cold, heat, tastes and smells, just as we can perceive sounds and sights. What is written in this chapter can be taken to apply to all the various senses, although it is easiest to take examples from visual experience.

Most people would hold that if an object can be seen in a clear light, close enough to examine carefully and with enough time to do so, then our awareness of it would give us an accurate representation of it. Figure 1 appears to be a spiral. There seems no doubt about it; it looks like a spiral however it is viewed. Yet in fact it is nothing of the kind. This can be proved by tracing the end of a pencil or stylus along the apparently spiral track, and it will be found that the path is a series of concentric circles.

It seems therefore that our awareness of the world around us is dependent not only on the external stimulation we receive from our sense organs, but also on a number of internal psychological factors. It is to these that we must now turn.

The Spiral Illusion

Fig. 1

Change or Discontinuity of Sensory Stimulation is Essential to Perception

Perception is a response to some change or difference in the environment. If the world were perfectly homogeneous, if nothing were different from anything else, if nothing changed with the passage of

time, then we should experience nothing. As long as atmospheric
pressure is experienced uniformly all over the body, we are not aware
of it. The 3-lb. per square inch felt by aviators at 40,000 feet is no
different from the 15-lb. per square inch felt at ground level, or the
50-lb. per square inch felt by men working in diving bells. But if the

An Impossible Perspective

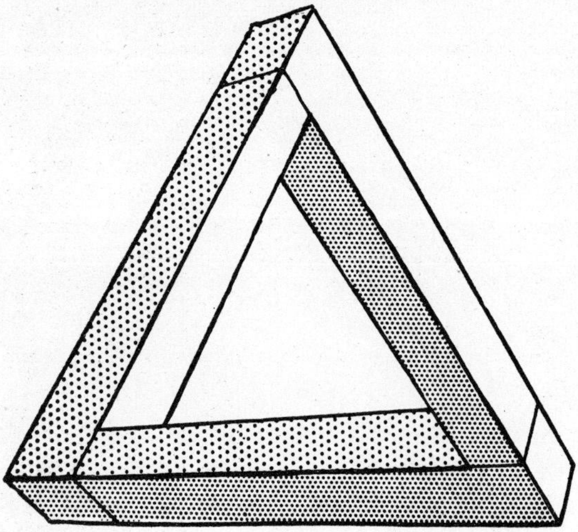

Fig. 2

50-lb. per square inch were felt on the hand alone, when the rest of the
body was being subjected to the more usual 15-lb. per square inch, it
would immediately be experienced as intense pressure. A loud clock
ticking continuously in a room ceases to be noticed after a few minutes,
but our attention is immediately drawn to it when it stops. We do not
react to stimulation as such, but rather to *change* in stimulation. We
make sense of our surroundings, see it in depth with objects against a
background, see it with colour and form, texture and shading, just
because there are a multitude of spatial discontinuities: changes of
colour and shade, shape and texture, edges and movement. If a
person's visual field is rendered homogeneous by sitting him in front
of a screen which is uniformly illuminated, he rapidly becomes unaware
of the screen some distance in front of him, and experiences instead a
dense fog in which he appears to be sitting.

Perception is Dependent on Past Experience and Learning

When we look at an object we never see it, as it were, with an innocent eye. We always view it with a wealth of past experience behind us. We see a chair, and we perceive that it is made of wood, that it has four legs, that its purpose is to be sat upon, that it is smooth, heavy and so on. Yet as we look at it, the stimulation we receive from the chair is visual only. This can tell us nothing directly about the material it is made of, nor its use as a piece of furniture, not its tactile properties, weight and so on. All we can become directly aware of is its shape, size and colour. The other properties we perceive are in fact supplied by us from our past experience of chairs. We have learnt that objects of this general shape and colour are designed to be sat upon, that they are heavy to lift, and that they are smooth to the touch. Moreover the appearance of the chair is two-dimensional, from which we infer the third dimension receding into the distance. We infer three dimensions from two, whenever we see a perspective drawing. Figure 2 is an impossible perspective which makes us uneasy as we look at it because we cannot make sense of it. We think we can interpret it, only to find that our interpretation is faulty as we shift our eyes to another part of the figure.

Whenever we say that ice looks cold, food looks tasty, or concrete looks hard, we are depending on past experience to supply part of the present perception, and this experience resides in us and not in the object viewed. As a famous American psychologist once said: " When we look out of the window and say that it's going to rain, we should, to be accurate and objective in our observation, restrict our statement to saying that our visual field is mottled blue and grey." We tend then to interpret the data supplied to us by our senses in terms of what we have learned in the past. Figure 4 is simply figure 3 printed upside down, yet the parts of the tank which appear to be bumps in one figure appear to be dents in the other and vice versa.

Since we interpret present sense data in terms of our own past experience, it follows that different people must have different perceptual worlds, each resulting from his own personal interpretation of the sense data he receives, based on his own personal store of past experiences. For example a married man with a family will surely appear very differently to his mother, his wife and his daughter, since each has had a very different set of experiences of the man in question. He will be seen as son, husband or father as the case may be, and will actually *look* different to each person.

Bumps or Dents?

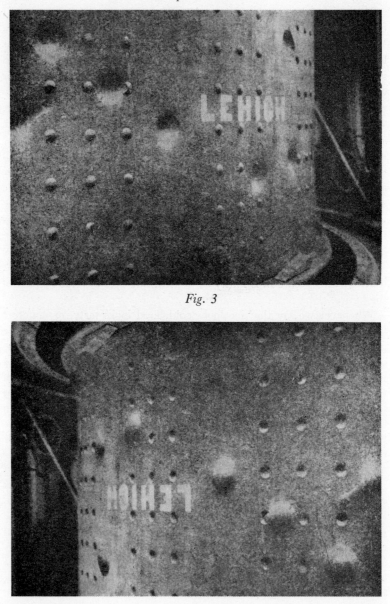

Fig. 3

Fig. 4

We thus perceive the world as we have learned to do. A toddler throwing a toy away in front of him, and then crawling after it, is learning all about the third dimension. A classic experiment on perception demonstrated this very convincingly. A psychologist wore prismatic spectacles which not only turned his visual field upside down, but also reversed it from left to right. He had to learn that if he wanted

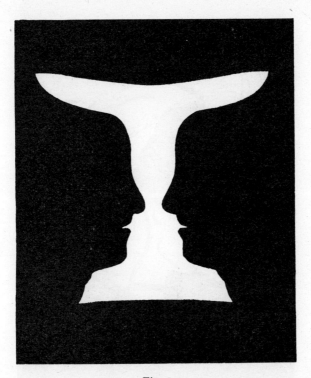

Fig. 5

something from the bottom right-hand corner of his visual field he had to reach up to the top left-hand corner. After some time he began to see the world for brief periods the right way up and the right way round. And after about a month he could move about as easily as he once could without the glasses on, because the world now looked the right way up and the right way round all the time. However when he was allowed to remove his spectacles the world now looked upside down and the wrong way round *without* the spectacles.   He perceived the world as he had learned to perceive it.

Sense Data are Organised by the Perceptual Process

Sense data can be distorted, modified, added to, and generally altered in all sorts of ways during the perceptual process.   Thus similar sensations can give variable perceptions.   A given figure or picture can

Old or Young?

Fig. 6

be seen in more than one way, according to how we organise it perceptually.   Figure 5 is a famous example of this, and is known as "Rubin's Vase".   This can be seen as a white vase or as two black faces looking at one another.   Figure 6 is a picture of a woman, but the question is " How old is she ? " Some see her as young, some see her as old. In fact there are two women in this drawing, some people see one and some the other. Not only can similar sensations give variable perceptions, but different or changing stimulation can be perceived in

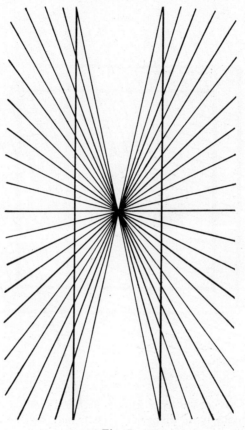

Fig. 7.

an unchanging way. If we watch a car coming towards us the retinal image of that car is rapidly increasing in size, but we do not see the car as swelling. We interpret its change in size in terms of its decreasing distance from us. It is quite easy to produce confusion between size and distance by reducing the perceptual cues involved. If we have someone look down a tube at a balloon illuminated from inside by a small light bulb, we can blow the balloon up and the person is quite likely to think that he has seen the balloon come down the tube towards him. This phenomenon of the unchanging perception despite the changing retinal image it yields, is known as " size constancy ". Other constancies are easily demonstrated. If we walk round a chair and view it from different angles, the shape of the image of that chair

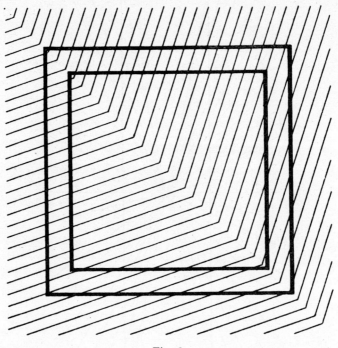

Fig. 8

on our retinae is constantly changing, yet we do not perceive the chair as actually changing in shape. The chair may well be illuminated so that it is in shadow in places and is high-lighted in other parts. Yet we do not see the chair as parti-coloured, but as variously illuminated.

The spiral illusion shown in the first figure in this chapter is a famous example of how our eyes can be deceived by quite simple arrangements of lines and patterns. The next two figures, Figure 7 and Figure 8, show two well-known illusions. The first of these shows how radiating lines can make two straight parallel lines look as if they were bowed outwards. The second shows a perfect square placed against a background which distorts it and makes it look out of true.

We have already seen how we tend to interpret what we perceive in terms of our past experience, and that our perception is largely a result of learning. This interpretation on the basis of past experience leads us to fill in gaps in our sensory data with data that are not actually sensed but are nevertheless " perceived ". If we look at a desk covered with books, we should be prepared to swear that the desk had a continuous surface on which the books lay. We have no direct sensory evidence of this, because much of the surface is in fact covered by the books, and cannot be seen. Yet the desk top " looks " continuous and solid. Conjurors make great use of this capacity of people to fill in what they do not actually sense. When we see a conjuror stuffing a silk handkerchief into a box, we assume the box is as other boxes with solid sides, and so on. We do not realise that this particular box has one side hollow, and that the conjuror is stuffing the handkerchief into the space between two thin walls. Another favourite trick which again depends on the fact that we perceive more than our senses tell us, is played with cards which are divided diagonally from corner to corner, one half of which is printed with spades and the other with hearts. When the cards are fanned out all we see are the spades. We assume that they are cards like other cards, and that the parts remaining hidden are printed with spades like the parts we can see. Again we might well be prepared to swear in a court of law that what we saw was a set of spades. The conjuror has only to turn the cards round and fan them out again, and we now see different cards in his hand, this time a set of hearts.

Perception is Selective

We have seen how we modify sense data, distort it, and interpret it in the light of past experience. But there is a great deal of sensory stimulation that we ignore and do not notice. Those who wear spectacles are usually unaware of the rims which lie well within the field of vision. Nevertheless if they wish, they can at any time pay attention to them, when they will again be noticed. We do not, however, walk around constantly aware of the rims of our spectacles. Most people, if they close one eye and look straight ahead, can see the tip of the nose within the field of vision. Yet we do not walk around aware of our noses sticking out in front of us. We are, in fact, constantly being bombarded by stimulation which we ignore: the clothes rubbing on our skin, the low murmur of people talking in the room next door, the creak of furniture, the hiss of a gas fire. We only notice those particular patterns of stimuli which are of importance and interest to us at the moment. Life would be intolerable if we were not able to do this. A family looking at a shop window of mixed goods will all notice different items in the window. The man will notice the carpentry tools, the woman the cosmetics or domestic goods, the schoolboy the model railway, and the small girl the doll. There is some evidence to show that this process of filtering off the unwanted stimulation is mediated by the reticular system (see Chapter 6).

The Effects of Motivation and Mood on Perception

The pattern of things we perceive will be greatly modified by habit, past experience and future intentions. For example, if a man wishes to leave a room, he will perceive those objects relevant to his aim: the furniture in the way, or the position of the handle on the door. He is not likely to notice the fly on the ceiling even if it happens to be in his field of vision, nor the pattern of the wallpaper. We all adopt perceptual " sets ", as they are called, and these are dictated by our interests, our desires of the moment, and even by our moods. It is everybody's experience how dull and drab the world seems when we are depressed, and how cheerful and gay when we are elated. This must be partly due to the fact that in the gay mood we notice the bright colours and the cheerful smiles, and when we are gloomy we notice the dirt in the gutter or the peeling paintwork.

All this has clear relevance to medical work. The doctor examining a patient has some very definite mental sets, leading him to notice small signs which would be completely missed by the layman. On the other hand he must be careful not to fill in perceptually in the way described above, and thus to perceive signs and symptoms which are not actually sensed, but only inferred from past experience.

Percepts and Images

We can look at an object and become aware of its shape, size and colour. We can touch it and become aware of its texture, whether it is hard or soft, cool or warm. We can lift it and become aware of its weight. But we can also put it down, step back from it, shut our eyes and imagine what it looks like in the mind's eye. We can imagine what it would feel like to the touch, or how it would feel when we lifted it and tested its weight. Now these two processes of perceiving and imagining are clearly distinct and easily distinguished under normal circumstances. We have defined perception as the awareness of objects which ensues upon the stimulation of sense organs. Imagery is not based on the present stimulation of sense organs, although we cannot imagine anything we have not previously perceived. A man blind from birth can have no idea what colour or visual shape can be like. It is true that we can imagine creatures we have never seen, nor could ever see, such as a lion with a giraffe's neck and a fox's tail. But this is merely the compounding of a complex image from a series of elements each of which have been perceived in the past.

Apart from the external criterion of whether the awareness is backed by stimulation of the sense organs or not, our experience of percepts and images under normal circumstances is quite different. Percepts are more real, more lively, more substantial than our images. Our percepts are located outside us, while our images are located " in the head " as it were. Our percepts can be further examined in a way that our images cannot. If we perceived something, and were asked for further information about it, we could obtain this by further examination. This is not usually possible with images. We cannot further examine them for added information. People with good imagery and retentive memories can give a great deal of information about things they have seen in the past and can now see in their mind's eye, but they cannot tell you about features of the object they did not previously perceive. We can always re-examine our percepts to gain fresh information about them we did not originally notice.

Moreover we can change our images as we please. A man can imagine his desk in front of him in his mind's eye, and can cover his image of it with five-pound notes: a thing that cannot be done with percepts. Thus images are usually under the control of the will: we can imagine what we please. We can summon them and dismiss them. Our percepts are only modifiable within very strict limits, as we have seen earlier in the chapter. Such things as reversible perspectives and ambiguous figures are changeable, but little else. Now these differences are important when we come to study abnormal perception and imagery. In certain circumstances the experiences of perception and imagery become confused so that a person may think he perceives what he only imagines, as in hallucinations, or he thinks he only imagines what he is really perceiving, as in some half-dream or twilight states. It is quite easy to arrange a situation when a perfectly normal person will " see " what in fact he is only imagining. This can occur at the sensory thresholds, when the intensity of stimulation is such that the stimulus is only just perceived. In this situation, it is sometimes difficult to say whether a light has really been seen or a sound heard, or whether such experiences have only been imagined. Under situations of emotional stress too, percepts and images are likely to be confused, especially when the intensity of the stimulation has been somewhat reduced. A timid person walking down a dark lane at night will tend to see every dark shape as a robber lurking to attack. This is a muddle between the fearful image and the innocuous percept.

People vary widely in their ability to summon up images of past sensory stimulation. Some can experience not only vivid scenes in the mind's eye, but music and other sounds in the mind's ear. Some can obtain vivid imagery of touch, taste and smell. Visual imagery is the most common, and olfactory imagery the least. As we shall see in Chapter 3, the use and manipulation of images of one kind or another is an important part of thinking, and although it may not be an essential part, many people are enormously helped in their thinking by seeing things in their mind's eye, or hearing them in their mind's ear. Since people vary so widely in the type and extent of their imagery, it follows that people with very different imagery might find difficulties in communicating with one another if they have to exchange ideas of any complexity. It seems clear that the widely different appeal that certain poets have to people may be partly due to their choice of imagery. A " visual " poet like Tennyson might have little appeal to a person who had little or no visual imagery, because he might be unable to conjure up the appropriate imagery as he read the poetry. Or when a poet writes of the " comfortable smell of fingers ", this must lose much of its appeal to the reader with no olfactory imagery.

SELECTED BIBLIOGRAPHY

1. *The Psychology of Perception*. Vernon, M. D. 1962. London: Pelican.
2. *Imagination and Thinking*. McKellar, P. 1957. London: Cohen and West.

Chapter 3

THINKING AND LANGUAGE

Thinking in Images

We saw in the last chapter how we can entertain visual and other forms of imagery; and we could be said to be thinking whenever we are aware of imagery of any kind, even when we are sitting back allowing our images to come and go in an idle fashion as we do when we day-dream. Often we indulge in day-dreams for our own amusement as when we remember some past experience and savour it again in retrospect. We then say we are " thinking " of last year's holiday, or of the party we went to last week. This sort of recollective thinking is very common in old people. But more strictly speaking we mean by " thinking " that we are entertaining a series of more or less logically connected ideas which have been initiated by a problem we wish to solve, and which are controlled and directed with the solved problem as the goal in view.

Now we have seen that it is possible to control imagery and to manipulate images as we please. Francis Galton in his classic study of imagery, was able to show that many practical ideas and problems could be thought about and solved by the use of images. For example if I wanted to change the furniture about in my room, I do not have actually to move the furniture into the various possible positions in order to try out the effect of such moves. I need only imagine it done in my mind's eye, and thus arrive at an idea of what the effects of various possible changes might be. If we had to describe the various changes to ourselves in words, we might find it very tedious. On the other hand, less practical and more abstract ideas are very difficult if not impossible to think of pictorially in this way. If we wanted to think about the concept " honesty " there is no single pictorial image which would adequately express this idea to us. Galton found that the more intellectual type of person who was used to thinking in abstract rather than concrete terms, usually reported that he had less pictorial imagery when he thought, than the more practical type of person. People who think in abstract terms have to use verbal imagery when they think: that is, words seen in the mind's eye, or heard in the mind's ear, or even felt as incipient movements in the larynx and throat. Many people talk to themselves silently when they think, or even whisper or talk aloud if they are alone.

Abstract and Concrete Thinking

This difference between abstract and concrete thinking is an important one with medical implications in certain forms of psychiatric and physical illness. One can think, for example, about a number of particular chairs: a desk chair, an arm chair, a dentist's chair, or a throne. But one can also think about chairs in general and thus form a concept of a chair which covers all the possible particular instances of it. Once this concept is formed, one can recognise an object as a chair although one has never seen a chair of that particular shape, size, colour or design before. This concept " chair " now covers all objects designed to be sat upon by one person, usually with a back and sometimes with arms. The concept " furniture " is more complex still, including other types of object as well as chairs. The term now includes all objects manufactured for use in dwellings which are not fixtures to the building. Primitive languages tend to multiply words for specific concrete objects, and to avoid the use of a single word to express a concept which might cover a large number of particular instances. Some African languages have no generic word for " cattle ", but instead employ a different word for each particular example of cattle according to its age, sex, size, colour, species and so on. To some extent we do the same in that farmers in various parts of the country use a large variety of names for different kinds of sheep, pigs, or horses. We speak of a colt, filly, mare, stallion and gelding. It is clearly more economical to use such words than have to qualify the generic term " horse " every time we wished to refer to a specific instance. On the other hand we should find it difficult if we had no generic word at all. While we must clearly be able to name particular objects, we must also be able to form abstract concepts of whole classes of objects.

Various forms of brain injury will reduce a patient's capacity to think abstractly, or to use concepts (see Chapter 19). This is revealed when he is asked to define words which he is only able to do in concrete terms. For example he will not define a table as an article of furniture, but may say: " That's what I have my tea on." Or he may be unable to define an apple as a fruit, but only as " Something to eat ". In the same way he may be unable to say in what way an apple resembles an orange, but may insist that they are totally unlike: one is an apple and the other is an orange. As well as in cases of brain damage, this inability to think abstractly is also seen in young children, in old people who have become senile and in the very dull. This difficulty in thinking abstractly takes rather a different form in some types of mental illness. Here the difficulty is not so much that the patient cannot think abstractly, but he does so inaccurately. His abstract notions may include particular instances which do not properly belong to the concept. This is called " over-inclusion ". For example such a patient, given the concept " house " and a series of words such as roof, wall, carpet, ceiling, chair, floor, window, curtain; will insist that the articles of furniture are equally necessary to the concept of house as are the walls, ceilings and windows. An example of this occurred when a patient was asked to say what shapes a complex pattern of inkblots reminded him of. He said that it looked rather like two women shopping, with a bus receding into the distance between them. This was quite a good response to the blot, but he spoilt it by adding that if the blot that looked like the back of a bus were not in fact a bus, then the two shapes that looked like women could not in fact be women. The similarity of two of the blots to women was not, of course, affected in the least by the similarity of the third shape to a bus receding into the distance.

A high level test of abstract thinking consists in the task of matching proverbs. Here the person may be asked to select two out of the following seven proverbs which mean the same.

> A bird in the hand is worth two in the bush.
> First come, first served.
> No man can serve two masters.
> As the twig is bent so will the tree grow.
> The early bird catches the worm.
> It's an ill wind that blows nobody any good.
> Still waters run deep.

To spot that the second and the fifth proverbs mean the same involves quite high level abstract thinking. It also involves a fair mastery of words, and some people fail tests of this kind, not necessarily because they cannot think abstractly, but rather because they have not been taught to use words fluently as tools for thinking. Again, in some forms of mental illness, patients develop a disordered form of thinking to the extent that this sort of verbal skill is disrupted, and unlikely or illogical connections are seen between proverbs that are not in any way similar in meaning.

Associations

We must now discuss another type of thinking which as we shall see in Chapter 4, has an important bearing on learning and memory. This is the phenomenon of association. This is something which has been noted and written about since the days of Aristotle. If we experience two things at the same time, or close together in space, they become associated in the mind, so that if we later experience one of them, or think of one of them, we tend to think of the other. Word association tests reveal the nature of these associations very quickly. If we ask a group of people to write down the first word that comes to their mind after each of the words: cat, black, up, chair, bat, and knife; they are very likely to say: dog, white, down, table, ball and fork respectively. It seems that people in the same culture, exposed to the same environmental influences tend to form very similar associations. Needless to say many more than one word or idea is associated with any given word or idea, but the strength of association between one word and various others are different. Thus knife may well be strongly associated with fork, but less so with such words as sharp, jack, or steel, and not at all with such words as sea, child or roof.

In any case many words we think of, or ideas we have in other than verbal form, carry with them a train or cloud of associations, some closely associated, some more tenuously. Moreover, many such associations will be emotionally toned, and carry pleasant or unpleasant feelings (see Chapter 7). We could never be aware of all these associations at any one time, although we may well be aware of an unpleasant feeling attached to some word or idea without quite knowing why. This accounts for the fact that we are sometimes aware of feelings of pleasure or annoyance or even disgust when we think of certain ideas, without being aware of the associations which have given rise to such emotion. These associations need not be words, but might just as well be visual images or memories of smells, sounds, or tastes.

Emotional Use of Words

Poets are well aware of this, and use words which are likely to have appropriate associations for us: appropriate, that is, to the mood they wish to engender in their readers. Thus Tennyson's line: " After many a summer dies the swan ", would be ruined if he had written " After many a summer dies the duck ". The associations we have for the word " swan " are so very different from those of the word " duck ". Any ribald paraphrase can reduce fine poetry to ruins. Thouless, in his book *Straight and Crooked Thinking*, points out that Keats' lines:

" Full on this casement shone the wintry moon
And threw warm gules on Madeleine's fair breast "

could have been just as well expressed, though less poetically, by the lines:

" Full on this window shone the wintry moon
Making red marks on Jane's uncoloured chest."

Words, then, have emotional associations which impart additional meaning to them. We may remark that we saw Smith *waiting* at the end of the road, or we might say that we saw him *lurking* at the end of the road. Both words mean much the same, but have very different emotional overtones. This could happen in medical note taking. We might write down that Mrs. Jones complains of several symptoms, or we might note down that she whines about her aches and pains. A psychiatrist might note that a patient says that he does not experience any hallucinations; or he might note down that the " patient denies hallucinations ", a thing in fact which most of us would do.

With a careful choice of words it is possible to speak the literal truth and yet give a totally different impression. This can be done without any sarcasm whatever. A mate of a cargo boat was logged for being persistently drunk. He reacted to this by reporting in the ship's log that the captain had appeared on duty sober that morning.

Unconscious and Creative Thinking

There seems to be a good deal of evidence that some problems can be solved at the unconscious level. Many people have had the experience of " sleeping on a problem " and waking up with their course of action clearly mapped out for them. (See Chapter 13.) A celebrated example of this occurred when the chemist Kekulé was doing research on the composition of benzene. He had puzzled for some time how six hydrogen and six carbon atoms could possibly be arranged in a chain and yet leave all the valencies satisfied. One night he is said to have had a dream in which he saw a long worm wriggling through water. Suddenly it curled round and gripped its own tail with its mouth. Kekulé woke up with a start realising that he had his answer to the problem. The benzene molecule was a ring. This sort of thing should teach us to be cautious about being too critical of hunches and intuitions. They may have a good logical basis, although such may not be immediately obvious to the thinker.

Some writers suggest that there are two distinctive types of thinking, one realistic and the other imaginative. In the former we are bound by logical rules and realistic possibilities; in the other we give free rein to our fancies and play about as it were, with our ideas, regardless of any rules of logic. Several studies have been made of the thinking of creative artists and scientists, and it seems that both types of thinking are employed by such people. A good deal of hard preparatory work has to be done, then the ideas are played about with imaginatively. This leads in some cases to new ideas or insights, which in their turn require hard logical thinking to turn them into practical possibilities. The successful creator can use both kinds of thinking productively. The strict logician, bound by rules and scientific method, remains in his groove. The undisciplined dreamer never gets his ideas into practical shape, and they remain only fantasies.

Problem-solving

We have seen that thinking often takes place when we have a problem to solve, so that it is appropriate in this chapter to say something about problem-solving. Some writers have suggested that we can only be said to be really thinking when we are presented with a problem that requires solution. If we are just allowing our imagination to drift along entertaining fantasies, we cannot be said to be thinking. This is a matter of definition, and we can get over this by speaking of realistic and imaginative thinking. Realistic, logical thinking, is what we have to use when solving problems, although even then, as we have seen, it may be necessary to indulge in some free imaginative thought, when we are seeking new leads or ideas.

One famous animal experimenter, Thorndike, put some hungry cats into puzzle boxes, from which they could see and smell some food through the bars. They struggled to get at the food, and sooner or later they pulled a loop of string hanging down inside the cage which released the latch fastening the door. This was done again every time the cat became hungry, and it was found that gradually the cat made fewer random movement before he pulled the string, until finally on being put into the box he would pull the string at once in order to get free. If a curve were drawn of the successive times taken to escape from the box, it would look something like Figure 9. This is known as a " trial and error leaning curve ", so called because the animal in this sort of situation appears to learn by trial and error. Woodworth defined this form of learning by saying that it had six distinguishing characteristics:

1. The animal (or human) must have a set towards a certain goal.
2. There must be no obvious direct route to that goal.
3. The situation must be explored in a more or less random fashion.
4. By chance, " leads " or " clues " to the means of reaching the goal must emerge.
5. Some of these leads must be tried out; those which work are retained and those which are not are dropped.
6. A correct lead is found and the goal is reached.

In certain situations we may use this type of behaviour in order to solve problems. Many people quickly lose patience with those types of puzzle consisting of two or more pieces of metal bent to odd shapes which have to be disentangled. They juggle the two bits until

for no obvious reason they come apart. The problem has
:d by trial and error, with no obvious insight as to how it
they were to repeat that problem many times, they might,
.ts, produce a trial and error learning curve.
r situations where the nature of the problem is more obvious,
have a better chance of seeing what is involved, they might
uite a different learning curve. Köhler, who did some classic

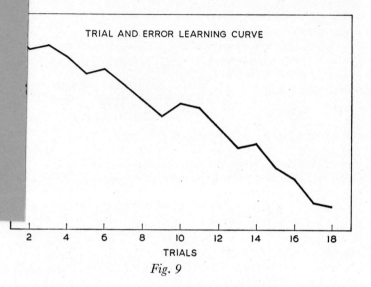

Fig. 9

work with chimpanzees, was able to show that these animals can solve
problems in quite a different manner, provided that they could see all
round the problem. Köhler placed a chimpanzee in a cage such that
bananas were only available by being pulled into reach with a stick.
Once the animal had learned to use the stick as a tool for this purpose,
he was placed in a situation where the food could only be obtained by
raking it in with a larger stick which itself was only obtainable by being
raked in by a stick too short to reach the food. The chimpanzee then
realised that he could use the shorter stick to get the longer stick, which
in turn could be used to get the food. In the final experiment the
animal was given two sticks which could only be used to rake in food
if they were fitted together to make one long stick. The animal in
question after a good deal of cogitation solved this problem too. Now
when he was given the problem to solve again the next day, he did it
without hesitation. This is obviously a very different way of learning

from that seen in Thorndike's cats. In the case of the chimpanzee, the successful response appears quickly and usually rather suddenly, and is not forgotten. In this case the learning curve would appear like Figure 10. This is known as an "insight learning" curve. Some psychologists have objected to the use of the term insight to this kind of learning, partly on the grounds that insight involves some kind of symbolic thinking, and there is no evidence one way or the other to

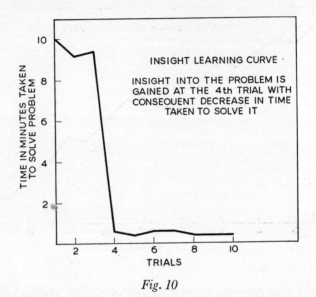

Fig. 10

suggest that animals are capable of symbolic thought. Nevertheless, there is no doubt that human beings can solve problems by gaining insight into their nature and the factors involved, and that if learning curves were drawn of problems solved by human beings in this way, they would look very like the ones achieved by Köhler's apes. To return to the little problem referred to earlier, of trying to separate two pieces of metal: with a little patience it is possible to gain insight into how the pieces of metal are entangled, and so to discover how they are to be twisted in order to separate them. Once this is done, the problem can be solved quickly and unhesitatingly on future occasions.

Problems are not usually solved solely by either method. Most are solved by a mixture of both trial and error and insight. For example we can solve a problem by trial and error, and then gain insight retrospectively: realising afterwards how it was solved, partly perhaps by logical reasoning, but also possibly by that sudden intuitive realisation of the nature of the problem said to be characteristic of insight.

SELECTED BIBLIOGRAPHY

1. *The Psychology of Thinking*. Thomson, R. 1959. London: Pelican.
2. *Straight and Crooked Thinking*. Thouless, R. H. 1935. London: English University Press.
   (Also available in a paperback edition.)

Chapter 4

LEARNING AND REMEMBERING

Learning, Instinct and Maturation

We saw in the last chapter that in trial and error learning those actions which are successful are retained, and those which are not are dropped. This was a vital factor in Thorndike's theory of learning. He said that those actions which were rewarded by success were " stamped in " to the animal's repertoire of movements, and those which were unsuccessful were " stamped out ". As we shall see, this concept of reward appears again in more modern theories of conditioning, in the guise of " reinforcement ". This is all good common sense, because we know from our own experience that when we are learning a new skill, or trying to solve a problem, those actions which are successful are the ones we remember. We soon give up trying ways of solving problems which do not pay off. Reward or reinforcement then, are vital factors in learning.

Learning is a process whereby behaviour is changed as a result of past experience. Such change is relatively permanent, a lesson would not be counted as learnt if it were soon forgotten. This term has to be distinguished from at least two others, one of these is *instinct* and the other is *maturation*.

Instinct is a term which refers to complex, innate patterns of behaviour which occur mainly in animals, and which do not appear to have been learnt. An obvious example is nest building in birds. Young birds do not see nests being built, yet the following year they build nests of a pattern recognisably characteristic of their species both in shape, size and the nature of the materials used. This pattern is variable within limits, in that if the customary nesting places or the usual materials are not available, birds will substitute other materials and choose other nesting places. Lower down the phylogenetic scale, instinctive behaviour is much less adaptable in insects, many of which are quite incapable of surviving in any but the most strictly suitable circumstances. At the other end of the scale, man himself can hardly be said to show instinctive behaviour in the ordinary sense of the word, but even he shows what one psychologist called " instinctive propensities ". That is, you do not have to teach a man to escape from danger, although the method he chooses to do so may vary from running screaming down the street, to quietly going off to the travel agency and buying an air ticket to Australia.

Some modifications of behaviour cannot be said to be learnt in the ordinary sense, nor can they really be said to be instinctive, but arise because the body of the animal or human being is developing. A child will begin to walk when he is physically developed enough to do so, if at that stage he is taught to do so. He cannot walk before he is mature enough to do so, neither will he walk unless he is taught. This process is known as *maturation*: without which some skills could never be learnt.

Recent work with animals has shown that many of the patterns of behaviour which were once thought to be instinctive are not entirely so, but are in part dependent on environmental influences. A famous example was demonstrated by Lorenz who showed that goslings will follow the first large moving object they see after they have been hatched. This, of course, is usually their mother, but Lorenz was able to get goslings to follow him by ensuring that the first large moving object they saw was himself. This early rapid form of learning is known as *imprinting*.

Classical Conditioning

Many of the modern theories of learning depend on some discoveries made by Pavlov at the beginning of this century. He was a Russian physiologist who had been doing various experiments on dogs. These were fed regularly in the same sort of routine, and he noticed that the dogs would begin to show signs of excitement and even to salivate when they heard the attendant's footsteps in the passage outside the laboratory, some moments before they could see, smell or taste the food. They had come to associate the sound of the man's footsteps with the meal itself. This of course is a commonplace sort of obervation, familiar to all who have kept a dog. The word " walk " or the sight of a leash will often send a dog into a state of great excitement in anticipation of a walk. However, Pavlov saw that something important had been observed, and began to study the phenomenon more closely. He was interested, as a physiologist, in studying possible neural connections in so-called reflex behaviour, and this seemed a possible method of doing so. He argued that with inexperienced dogs, the sound of footsteps would not normally cause them to salivate. If they now salivated when they heard footsteps, this must mean that a new stimulus had become potent in producing the original response.

The classical experimental situation was as follows. The dogs were given a simple surgical operation so that the salivary duct of the parotid gland was brought to the surface of the cheek, and attached to a tube leading to a small graduated vessel, so that the rate of flow of saliva could be recorded. They were then constrained by a harness and isolated from extraneous stimuli. When they were hungry they were shown food and then fed. The rate of flow of saliva was noted. We can represent this situation as follows:

Food (sight, smell, taste) $\longrightarrow$ Salivation
Unconditioned stimulus   *Unconditioned response*

On future occasions the sight, smell and taste of food was accompanied by the sound of a bell, or the bell was sounded immediately beforehand. Once again the dogs salivated. This situation can now be represented thus:

Food (sight, smell, taste)
Unconditioned stimulus
plus $\longrightarrow$ Salivation
Bell (sound)   *Unconditioned response*
Conditioned stimulus

After this pairing of the bell and food had been done several times, the bell is now sounded alone, and the hungry dog now salivates even though he does not see, smell or taste the food. The situation now is:

Bell (sound) $\longrightarrow$ Salivation
Conditioned stimulus   *Conditioned response*

Before the conditioning process the dogs produced no salivation whatever when the bell sounded. Now they did, so a new behaviour pattern had been learned, and the reflex behaviour of the dogs had been modified. Pavlov went on to hypothesise about the various changes that must have taken place in the dogs' nervous systems to account for this. Because this happens at the reflex level, it might seem that this is something more than conscious association, and may happen without the animal's being aware of what is going on. Now it is impossible to talk about an animal being aware or not aware of his surroundings. We can only speak about his behaving as if he were aware. But it is possible, though much less easy, to produce conditioned reflexes in human beings. It is possible for example, to deliver a small puff of air to a person's eyelid so that he blinks reflexly. This puff of air can then be paired to a light or a buzzer, and people can then be made to blink when the light shines, or the buzzer sounds in the absence of the puff of air. This can be done without the subject's knowing that he has been so conditioned and without his realising that people have been making him blink in this way.

Some writers have given the impression that in conditioning, the original stimulus has been replaced by a new one, which produces exactly the same response as the original. They have claimed that in

conditioning there has been a full replacement of one stimulus by
another. Reference to Pavlov's original work shows this not to be the
case. The conditioned response is in fact something of a pale imitation
of the unconditioned one. Pavlov points out that the rate of flow of
saliva in the actual presence of food in the mouth is of the order of 3 to
4 c.c. a minute, but when the conditioned dog is responding merely to
the sight of food, the rate of flow is only of the order of about 0.7 c.c. a
minute. The conditioned response then, is a kind of preparatory
response, getting ready, as it were, for the expected food.

Pavlov then found that dogs who had been taught to respond to a
particular bell, would also respond to other bells, or even to sounds of
other kinds. This is the phenomenon of *generalisation*. Pavlov then

SKINNER
LEARNING.

n order to maintain the conditioned reflex it was necessary
rcement in the shape of food every so often. That is, the dog
e reminded, as it were, that the bell did mean food. If the
peatedly sounded in the absence of food, the reflex would
inction and disappear altogether. This made it possible for
the dogs to respond to bells of certain pitches by reinforcing
ses with food, and not to respond to bells of other pitches by
cement so that the response to these became extinguished.
rocess of *differentiation*. This gave Pavlov a powerful method
ng how acutely dogs could differentiate between various
found, for example, that dogs could differentiate without
tween two whistles so close in pitch that no difference was
to the human ear. They were also taught to salivate to a
ot to an ellipse. The ellipse was then gradually broadened
pproximated more and more to a circle. At one point the
not tell whether the shape was really a circle and that food
, or whether it was really an ellipse, and that no food was
cted. Some of the dogs in these conditions appeared to
nervous breakdown. They went out of condition, they
snapped and had to be sent away to a farm to recover.
erhaps the first time that an experimental neurosis had been
It might be held to throw some light on the genesis of
roses: we may break down when we have to make important
the basis of inadequate evidence.

l Conditioning

experimenter, Skinner, has more recently been continuing
work originally pioneered by Thorndike. In this, it will be
recalled, Thorndike put hungry cats into boxes from which they
escaped when they had performed the appropriate movement. Skinner
devised a rather simpler method of doing the same sort of thing, by

putting a hungry rat into a box in which there was a lever. The rat would roam about restlessly looking for an exit or for food, and by chance he would press the lever. This action would be rewarded by the appearance of a pellet of food. The rat soon learned to press the lever whenever it was hungry. This is known as instrumental conditioning, and is much more akin to conscious association and takes place above the reflex level. One can see how this sort of learning takes place all the time. We tend to repeat those actions which pay off, and discard those which are unsuccessful. A baby lying uncomfortable and restless in a cot may produce a number of random movements and noises. If mother comes every time it cries, then the child learns to cry when it wants attention. Skinner found, as Pavlov did, that a conditioned response can be extinguished if it is not rewarded. He also found that if the response were reinforced only every tenth time, that is the rat received food only at every tenth pressing of the lever, it was much more difficult to extinguish the response. This again sounds perfectly reasonable. If we know that we do not get the food every time we press the lever, we are not discouraged so easily by fruitless attempts. As long as we continue to think that occasionally we shall be rewarded, we are prepared to go on trying for much longer. This is a nice explanation of the success of the Football Pools. A small prize occasionally will keep us going: even other peoples larger prizes serve to reinforce our responses, and we go on paying out the weekly " investment ".

Remembering

Remembering refers to the recall of previous experience, usually in the form of imagery, verbal or otherwise, and thus has a narrower meaning than learning. Learning can occur without actually remembering as when we learn some motor skill such as cycling. We could hardly say that we remember how to ride a bicycle. If we had not ridden one for twenty years and were asked whether we could ride a bicycle, we could not say that we remembered how to do so, we could only say that we did not know until we tried.

The three phases of the memory process are often referred to as *Impression*, *Retention* and *Reproduction*. That is we have to learn the lesson, we have to record it in some way, and then it has to be recalled or recognised later. The recording of the lesson, or its retention for later recall, is still somewhat of a mystery, and little is known about this part of the process. Moreover we can never examine a brain and note the memories stored therein. Our only method of discovering how much has been retained by the learner is to get him to repeat the lesson later. Retention can be defined as " *the process whereby a persisting trace is left behind as an after-effect by any experience forming the basis of learning, memory, habit and skill, and of all development, so far as it is based on experience* " (Drever).

The Work of Ebbinghaus

In 1885 Ebbinghaus published a monograph on his studies of memory. These are worth mentioning because they were the first attempt to study the phenomenon in a systematic sort of way. He used nonsense syllables as the material to be learned. These consisted of a consonant on either side of a vowel, so that they were pronounceable, although meaningless. Examples might be:

POF, GEP, RIJ, VEC, TEF

and so on. He chose this sort of material because in earlier experiments he found that some material was much easier to learn than others. He accounted for this by saying that some material had more associations for the learner than others, and thus could be more easily

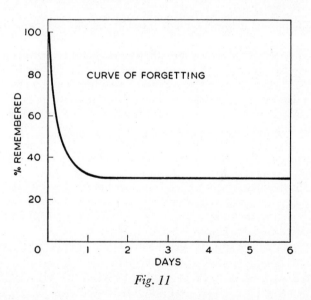

Fig. 11

remembered. He thought that nonsense syllables would get over this difficulty, and that the various lists of syllables used would all be of comparable difficulty.

He used novel methods of measuring retention. He would learn some lists of nonsense syllables until he could recite them perfectly twice. After an interval he would then learn them again, until he could once more recite them perfectly twice. If he took 1,000 seconds to learn them on the first occasion and only 600 seconds to learn them on the second, then the *saving* of time was 400 seconds. This saving could be a measure of the amount of material retained. This method had an obvious advantage over straight recall, since it would be a measure of retention even in cases where people could not recall any part of a previous lesson, but who nevertheless took a shorter time to re-learn it if they had seen it before. Ebbinghaus used several different intervals between learning and re-learning, varying from twenty minutes to thirty-one days. He was able to draw a curve of forgetting which looked something like Figure 11. Each point on the learning curve was produced by the learning and re-learning of a different list of nonsense syllables. Thus it was important to be able to assume that each list was of comparable difficulty. This curve of forgetting is logarithmic: it falls sharply at first, then more slowly, and finally levels out.

Factors in Impression

In Chapter 2 it was pointed out that *attention* was an important factor in perception. We did not perceive a thing unless we paid attention to it. It follows equally that we shall not remember anything unless we pay attention to it, because we could hardly recall anything we did not perceive in the first place. A stimulation is more likely to be attended to, and therefore remembered, if it is intense or prolonged. Shape, size and position of an object will affect whether or not it is noticed, and contrasting colours, sounds, tastes and smells and even textures are more likely to be noticed than when the stimulation is homogeneous. Any initiation or cessation of movement is likely to be attended to. This is why " blinking " trafficators on cars are so much more effective than the older type of semaphore trafficator. As Ebbinghaus discovered, material which was meaningless was more difficult to learn than something which made sense. Compare these two lists of words taken from Hunter's book on Memory:

TAS-YAL-DOP-SIW-MEL-YOS-HIW-LON-MAF-GIW-
NAL-WOH
WE-ALL-SAW-A-TINY-GOLD-FISH-WHO-SWAM-IN-
MY-POOL

There is no doubt which would be the easier to learn. Another of Ebbinghaus' discoveries was that if material is overlearnt, it is easier to recall later. *Overlearning* means learning material for longer than is necessary to produce perfect recitation of it. Mathematical tables, the alphabet and our own names and addresses are usually overlearnt.

If we are learning a part in a play, especially a well-known classic like Shakespeare in which many members of the audience will know the lines as well as the players, it is important to be word perfect. We have to achieve a literal reproduction of the material. This sort of learning is called *rote learning*, and was the type studied by Ebbinghaus. Mercifully we do not have to learn text-books in this way, indeed it might be dangerous to try to do so, since learning this way may mean that the student has little understanding of the material he has learned. In reading text-books it is more usual to get the gist of what it is all about, so that it can be reproduced in our own words. This second type of learning is sometimes referred to as *content learning*. Both rote and content learning arise from deliberate effort. It is sometimes possible to find that one has learnt something without making any deliberate effort to do so. This is called *incidental learning*. This is fairly common in young children, who learn nursery rhymes and even whole story books in this way. Many parents have been thoroughly chided by their young children for varying their reading of *Peter Rabbit* by a single word. This happens often before the child can read himself at all.

Some lessons are so striking that one is enough. " Once seen never forgotten " applies to certain shock experiences which are so vivid that a single experience is enough to fix the memory for a lifetime. Material frequently experienced is more easily retained than lessons only ocassionally learnt. If rote learning is to be undertaken, like a part in a play, recitation is often a help. That is you learn the first line or sentence, then recite it from memory. Then you learn the second line and recite the first two, and so on. Thus you recall what you have already learnt at regular intervals. This seems to be more efficient than merely reading the speech or passage over and over. For content learning, on the other hand, it is necessary to organise the material; to classify, summarise, code, select, or emphasise. You have to pick out the important points in the material, and see them as figures standing out against the general background of argument, exposition, or example. Mnemonics are helpful in some forms of rote learning as all medical students know.

So far we have been discussing characteristics of the material to be learnt, and of ways of handling it. We must now say a word about some aspects of the learner himself. An important factor will clearly be his interest and motivation. The incentive of a coming examination will motivate a student to learn material which he would otherwise reject as boring beyond measure. On the other hand material which the learner finds intrinsically interesting, will be absorbed without difficulty in the absence of any external incentive like examinations.

The physiological state of the learner: excitement, fatigue, or illness, will clearly affect his ability to assimilate new material, by making him distractible, sleepy, and disorientated. It is an unfortunate thing that the older we get the more difficult we find it to remember new material. The absorption of new facts, unrelated to our existing knowledge, is increasingly difficult after about the age of thirty-five or forty. New languages are relatively easily learned by children and young people, but they are rarely mastered in later life. The older we get the more slowly and less efficiently we learn. The ability to learn is of course related to intelligence. The cleverer a person is, the more easily he learns. This applies particularly to content learning, where the mastery of the material involves achieving an understanding of what it is all about. Rote learning is somewhat different. Some mentally deficient people are surprisingly good at rote learning.

Factors in Retention

Another interesting thing that Ebbinghaus discovered was that if a lesson were learnt, its retention could be seriously impaired by learning a second lesson in between the learning of the first lesson and its recall. This was especially likely to happen if the two lessons concerned were similar, for example, if they were both lists of nonsense syllables. This is known as *retroactive interference*. The first lesson can also interfere with the second, and this is known as *proactive interference*. This sort of difficulty is less likely to occur if the lessons are very different in character, for example if we sat down to learn a chapter in an anatomy book, and then went out and had a driving lesson. Retroactive interference would be more likely to occur if we learnt a chapter of a book on human bone structure, and then a chapter on the bone structure of the anthropoid apes. We might get the two sets of similar material muddled up.

People tend to remember things better if they do a little at a time, with frequent but not too prolonged rest pauses. Spaced is better than massed learning. Lessons also tend to be forgotten if they are not frequently rehearsed. That is, memories fade with time if they are not recalled at intervals.

Forgetting too, can be caused by sleepiness or intoxication at the time of impression. If we wake in the morning we may remember a dream, but unless we write it down then and there, we are apt to forget it. More strikingly still, a patient may have to be woken in the middle of the night for some examination, treatment or medication, yet not know a thing about it next morning. Equally a boozy party may only be dimly remembered next day, if at all. Concussion or

Electro Convulsive Therapy* (E.C.T.) (see Chapter 6) can cause people to forget events both before and after the insult. Very old or very young people are less likely to retain impressions than people between these extremes of age.

This amnesia, or inability to remember, is selective. It is the recent memories that tend to be lost rather than the remote ones. Concussion or E.C.T. tends to make a person forget a little of the immediate past (*retrograde amnesia*) and sometimes rather more of events that have happened after the accident or insult (*anterograde or post-traumatic amnesia*). These phenomena are discussed in greater detail in Chapter 6, it is only necessary to mention them here in order to provide evidence for what is known as *consolidation* as an important factor in retention. All the facts so far mentioned in connection with retention: retroactive interference, superiority of spaced over massed learning, the effects of sleepiness or intoxication at the time of impression, the effects of extremes of youth and age, and above all the selective nature of amnesia in that recent memories are lost more easily than remote ones: all these facts can be explained in terms of consolidation. In order to be retained a memory has in some way to be consolidated, rather as a negative on a photographic plate has to be fixed, otherwise it is lost. Indeed recent biochemical work suggests that the more permanent kinds of retention, in our terms the "consolidated memories", may involve actual changes in molecular structure of brain tissue. This is a process which takes time to occur (see Chapter 6).

Thus old memories are less vulnerable to the effects of concussion or E.C.T. because they have had more time to become consolidated. Moreover the concussed brain is less able to consolidate its memories, so post-traumatic amnesia occurs. The sleepy or intoxicated brain may, in the same way, be less able to consolidate memories. This is not just a case of the sleepy or drunk person not having assimilated the lesson in the first place. A sleepy person can wake up and record his dream, which he forgets later. A drunk or concussed person can behave rationally enough at the time, but cannot recall the period later. One study demonstrated that people who have just finished a course of E.C.T. can look at and describe a picture in good detail immediately afterwards, but are quite unable to recognise it later. Infants and very old people may again be unable to recall events that happen in their infancy or old age because their brains at that time are unable to consolidate memories.

The person who has just completed a course of E.C.T. and who can describe a picture he has just seen with fair accuracy, but who fails

---

* See Glossary.

to recognise it later, is demonstrating an important difference between two kinds of memory image. If a person is asked to repeat the number 96142 he can usually do so with ease by referring to the image of the number left in his mind's eye or heard in his mind's ear. This is known as the *primary memory image*. This is memory for immediately past events. This is different from the *revived memory image*, which is the one we recall afresh—rather than the one we hold on to immediately after impression. Primary memory images are not consolidated and do not have to be, although they may later become so. Indeed revived memory images may have to be consolidated if they are to be recalled at all. There are, of course, degrees of consolidation. Some memories seem barely consolidated, others very firmly so. As we have seen, it is usually the old material which is the better consolidated.

It is sometimes convenient, therefore, to divide memories into three categories: *immediate, recent,* and *remote*. *Immediate* memories refer to primary memory images; *recent memories* to the recall or recognition of experiences that have taken place in the fairly recent past; and *remote memories* refer to those old memories which have had time to become thoroughly consolidated and which are resistant to loss from any of the causes mentioned above.

Factors in Reproduction

Finally we must discuss the factors which operate in the reproduction of memories. First we must distinguish between recognition and recall. If we teach somebody a list of names of twenty animals so that he can recite them perfectly, we can then ask him to recite them at a later time. This is *recall*. But we could also present him with a list of forty animals, and ask him to pick out from the list the twenty he had seen previously. This would be *recognition*. Recognition is easier than recall, but is less accurate.

Association helps memory enormously. A prompter usually only needs to give an actor a word or two or a line of his part, and he can continue once again. The more rich the associations we have with an event the more likely we are to remember it. People who like to demonstrate their prodigious memories, often achieve their remarkable results by associating the material in strikingly unusual ways. Nonsense syllables can sometimes be remembered with ease by imagining each as a name for a series of friends. Suppose for example one knows two families each with four children. Now one has eight names already learnt. All one now has to do is to associate each nonsense syllable to one of the people; Mr. Smith is TAS, Mrs. Smith is YAL, John Smith is DOP, Sarah Smith is SIW and so on. Paired associations are surprisingly easy to learn. The trick here is to choose a series of names you already know, with which to pair the new material.

Remembering as a Reconstructive Process

In his book on " remembering ", Bartlett made a number of important observations. He pointed out that much of remembering was a reconstructive process, a true re-membering. We retained a general " schema " of the lesson and in recall we filled this in by interpretation, elaboration, and so on. Material was retained often in simplified and conventionalised form, and often in the form of some schema. We might be asked to recall what we saw of an accident. We might have remembered it thus: " There were two cars and one hit the other broadside on ". This would be the general schema retained. When we begin to remember it we tend to add details, not necessarily of what we saw, but of what we thought must have been the case: one car skidded and slewed round, the other tried to avoid him and braked. The schema would be a simplification of the original event, and this would be later elaborated in recall. If the thing to be remembered is strange or difficult to understand, we tend to recall it in more meaningful and conventional terms. Bartlett has a story he had people remember, involving canoes and paddles. The story was often later recalled as being about boats and oars. Anything which tends not to fit in with the general schema or which appears meaningless, tends to be forgotten. If people are given rather strange shapes to reproduce later, they tend to name the shape. Later when they reproduce it, it tends to represent the name given, rather than the shape itself. A rather vague shape which might be a cat sitting up, or a bird perched on a branch, is often named by people " cat " or " bird ", and this naming greatly affects the shape of the reproduction later.

Just as fatigue or the action of drugs can impair the impression or even perhaps the retention of a memory, it can also impair the recall. Sleepy or drugged people cannot always concentrate sufficiently to bring the memory to mind. Some drugs, however, the barbiturates for example, can in some cases actually facilitate the recall of forgotten material.

Freud suggested that unpleasant or unwelcome memories could be *repressed* into the unconscious (see Chapter 8) and so be forgotten. This mechanism of repression was itself unconscious, in that we did not consciously try and get rid of these memories. They just disappeared. A conscious attempt to get rid of unpleasant memories is known as *suppression*. If you listen to someone recalling a quarrel at which you have been present as a disinterested observer, it is fascinating to hear them omitting, often all too unconsciously, those parts of the argument in which they were worsted, and remembering those parts in which they triumphed. It would be intolerable if we remembered all our failures and none of our triumphs. It is a blessed dispensation of providence that we tend to do the opposite.

SELECTED BIBLIOGRAPHY

1. *The Psychology of Thinking.* Thomson, R. 1959. London: Pelican.
2. *Memory: Facts and Fallacies.* Hunter, I. M. L. 1957. London: Pelican.
3. *Remembering.* Bartlett, F. C. 1932. Cambridge University Press.

Chapter 5

INTELLIGENCE

It used to be thought that success in school-work was the result of diligence and hard work on the part of the pupil, coupled with good teaching on the part of the teacher. Failure on the other hand was held to be due to the laziness and moral turpitude of the pupil coupled with the incompetence of the teacher. Not unnaturally, therefore, teachers would take energetic steps to ensure that their pupils did not reflect their failings as teachers. This usually took the form of chastisement. This point of view lingers on, and there are still schools where children are given the strap or cane because they cannot do their lessons; their inability being attributed to laziness or carelessness.

As compulsory education began to be introduced, it became increasingly obvious that some children were less capable than others in their school work. These children made slower progress however hard they worked, and however amenable they were to discipline. Other children who seemed to work less hard, to pay less attention to their lessons and to be less amenable to discipline, nevertheless seemed to manage to learn more than the others and to learn it faster with less apparent effort. Some factor other than diligence and hard work seemed therefore to be operating. This factor came to be known as " intelligence ".

Mental Age and Intelligence Quotient

In 1905, the French psychologist Binet was given the task by the Paris education authorities of discovering those children who were too dull to be educated in ordinary schools. In order to do this he devised the first quantitative method for measuring intelligence, and related it to some sort of a scale. His method was a sensible and a relatively simple one. He argued that as children grew older, their abilities developed so that it should be possible to find various little tasks and problems which could only be solved when a child had matured sufficiently to master them. He set himself the task of finding out what the *average* child could do at various ages over the range he was testing. He found that the average child of six years could give his age, reproduce a sentence of sixteen syllables, count thirteen pennies, correctly copy a diamond shape and define a " horse " and " chair " in terms of their use. Children who could do these tasks, but who could not do any harder than these, were said to have a *mental age*, or M.A. of six, irrespective of their *chronological age*, or C.A. Thus a bright child of five might be able to do all these tasks and could then be said to have a mental age of six, while a dull child might not be able to manage them until he was seven, and he too would have a mental age of six. These children could then be compared for intelligence by calculating an *intelligence quotient* or I.Q. for each by expressing the mental age as a percentage of the chronological age.

For the six-year-old child passing the six-year tests, his I.Q. would be:

$$\text{I.Q.} = \frac{\text{M.A.} \times 100}{\text{C.A.}} = \frac{6 \times 100}{6} = 100$$

For the five-year-old, the I.Q. would be:

$$\text{I.Q.} = \frac{6 \times 100}{5} = 120$$

And for the seven-year-old, the I.Q. would be:

$$\text{I.Q.} = \frac{6 \times 100}{7} = 86$$

I.Q.'s remain fairly constant throughout life: bright children remaining bright and dull children remaining dull.

The Nature of Intelligence

About the same time as Binet, a British psychologist, Spearman, had begun work in this field, and in 1927 he gave a full statement of his theories and methods. Briefly, he said that people who were good at some tasks were often good at many others as well. He deduced from this that there was a general factor of ability common to all intellectual tasks. This is called the " general factor " " g ". He stated, moreover, that this ability consisted of two fundamental intellectual operations known as " the eduction of relations " and the " eduction of correlates ". (Eduction means the " drawing out ".) In other words: given two objects or ideas, we can educe the relation between them; or given one object or idea and a relation, we can educe the correlate.

Eduction of a relation:

An elephant is $\begin{cases} \text{smaller than} \\ \textit{larger than} \\ \text{the same size as} \end{cases}$ a mouse

Given the ideas of an elephant and a mouse, we can educe the correct relation between them. An elephant is *larger* than a mouse.

Eduction of a correlate:

$$\text{A foot is longer than } \begin{cases} \text{a mile} \\ \text{a yard} \\ \textit{an inch} \end{cases}$$

Given the idea of a foot and the relation " longer ", we can educe the correct correlate. A foot is longer than an *inch*.

Spearman produced a number of tests based on these principles, and it was found that children who did well on these tests were also found to do well in school-work and in examinations. These were the children whose teachers regarded them as being " clever " or " intelligent ".

Definitions of Intelligence

As with any rather complicated abstraction, the definitions of intelligence are many and various. Each emphasises some aspect of the concept, or is based on some theory. Binet, for example, regarded intelligence as a complex set of qualities, including such things as the appreciation of a problem, the capacity for making the necessary adaptations in solving it, and the power of self-criticism. Spearman based his definition on his own theory about the nature of intelligence, and defined it as " the ability to educe relations and correlates ". This definition has been expanded by Knight as follows: " The capacity for relational, constructive thinking directed to the attainment of some end."

Most psychologists are careful to distinguish intelligence from acquired knowledge, although of course the more intelligent a person is, the easier it is for him to acquire knowledge; and other things being equal the more likely it is that he will do so. Nevertheless, it is perfectly possible in theory for a person to be highly intelligent, and yet to remain relatively ignorant. Intelligence is thought of as a capacity or potential ability, something one has to a greater or lesser extent, rather than something that is acquired as a result of training. Even this is not the whole story. Hebb has distinguished between two aspects of intelligence: what he calls " genetic potentiality " or intellectual capacity ultimately determined by the genes; and " present mental efficiency " which, although not acquired in the same way as formal education and training, consists nevertheless of " cognitive abilities " which have been built up during infancy and childhood and which do not develop in the absence of environmental stimulation. It is therefore not quite accurate to define intelligence purely as inborn or innate mental ability. A vague definition is the only one that suits everybody. Such a definition is that of Vernon who defines intelligence as " general mental ability ".

An Intelligence Test

We shall get a better idea of the mental operations involved in intelligent behaviour if we have a look at the sort of items that constitute a typical intelligence test. The items in such a test which are described below are designed on Spearman's principles of the eduction of relations and correlates. Such items aim, as far as possible, to measure innate capacity apart from any knowledge acquired by the testee, and are held to be relatively unaffected by cultural or educational influences. Not all intelligence tests are of this kind. Other things being equal people of high intelligence tend to learn more than people of lower intelligence, so that any test of attainments such as an arithmetic or English test, might be quite a good measure of innate capacity. But this would only be a fair test if all the people tested had had equal educational opportunities. Since this is by no means always the case, it is often better in clinical work to use tests of innate capacity which are not heavily dependent on acquired knowledge. It is, of course, important to have a measure of a patient's acquired knowledge, but this, as we shall see, can be assessed by separate tests.

A typical item then, in a relatively " culture-free " test of innate capacity might be

1	2	3	Which of the following numbers
2	4	6	fit best at □
3	6	□	2, 6, 4, 3, 7, 9 or 10?

The answer is clearly 9, since the numbers progress regularly from left to right, and from top to bottom of the matrix. A rather harder example is this one:

H	L	P	Which of the following letters
K	O	S	fit best at □
N	R	□	Q, V, X, L, R, M, O or S?

Here the progression from left to right consists of every fourth letter in the alphabet, and the progression from top to bottom consists of every third letter in the alphabet. In either case the missing letter is V. In both items, of course, the testee can only answer if he knows the progression of numbers and the order of letters in the alphabet. It is a simple matter to arrange a series of such items with a very wide range of difficulty from primary school to university level. This type of test picks out the potentially successful pupil or student, but it tells us nothing about whether he or she has acquired any knowledge. As we have already observed, a person can be intelligent, and yet remain an ignoramus. It is therefore useful to give a test of acquired knowledge as well. It has been found that the best single pointer to a person's

educational level, is the size of his vocabulary. This can be estimated
by asking him to define a list of words of graded difficulty. Such a list
could begin with simple words in common use like " apple ", " chair ",
" hand ", " tree ", and so on, and end with more difficult ones like
" charivari ", " eclogue ", " parameter " or " transilient ". Again it
is a simple matter to arrange a series of such words over a wide range
of difficulty.

Both these types of test have to be standardised on a large sample of
the general population to discover the range of scores to be expected at
every age.

Distribution of Intelligence

The diagram below (Fig. 12) shows how intelligence is distributed
over the population. The graph shows I.Q.'s as measured by a modern

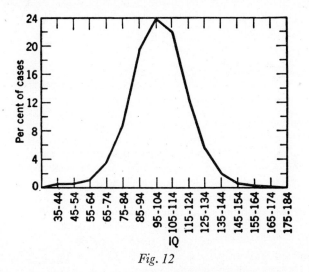

Fig. 12

form of the Binet scale, of 2904 unselected children between the ages
of 2 and 18 years. The majority of scores lie between I.Q. 75
and I.Q. 125. This sort of distribution is the expected one for all
measures which are randomly distributed. Similar curves would be
obtained for measures of the height and weight of adults in the general
population, or for groups of children at any given age. This is known
as the " normal distribution " and would occur if you tossed ten
pennies up a thousand times, and counted at each toss the number of
heads. You would get four, five or six heads a large number of times,
and ten or no heads very rarely indeed.

There is some evidence that intelligence is not quite as normally distributed as it appears from the graph, and that the way tests are constructed and scored may result in the normal seeming appearance of the curve. Some tests scored differently do not show quite such a symmetrical distribution, but tend to have rather more higher scores than lower ones. Moreover it appears that there are more very low scores than very high ones. The curve stretches out with a long tail at the lower end (Fig. 13).

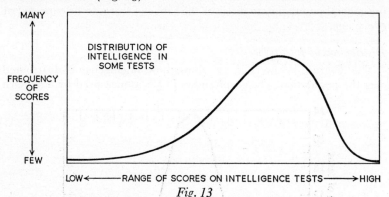

MANY

FREQUENCY
OF
SCORES

FEW

DISTRIBUTION OF
INTELLIGENCE IN
SOME TESTS

LOW ◄——————RANGE OF SCORES ON INTELLIGENCE TESTS——————► HIGH

Fig. 13

Changes of Intelligence with Age

When Binet and Spearman began applying their tests to a large range of ages, it soon became apparent that the upper limit of scoring on tests for innate capacity was reached rather earlier than had been expected. This age varies with the particular test used. On one test a person reaches his maximum score at the age of 14 or 15. On another test the score continues to increase until he is 25. However, on both these tests, the score declines steadily from the age of 25 onwards.

On the other hand, tests for acquired knowledge do not reach their maximum until about the age of 30 or 35 and may produce little or no decline, or even a slight increase over the whole of a person's working life. It is an unfortunate fact that dull people decline in ability more rapidly than bright people, both in innate capacity and acquired knowledge tests, although both bright and dull people decline more rapidly in innate capacity tests than in vocabulary tests. The average person of 70 does as well as a child of 8 in innate capacity tests, but an average 70-year-old knows as many words as a young person of 18.

Difficulties in the Use of "Mental Ages"

Earlier in this chapter we expressed the " Intelligence Quotient " or I.Q. as a percentage ratio of the mental to the chronological age.

We also said that the I.Q. so calculated remained relatively constant throughout life. It will now be seen that, if the mental age or M.A. as expressed by the test score ceases to increase after the age of 15 or so, I.Q.s will not remain constant if the chronological age or C.A. continues to be used in the calculation after that age. The following table shows what would happen to the I.Q. if this were done:

Table 1

C.A.	M.A.	I.Q.
5	5	100
10	10	100
15	15	100
20	15	75
25	15	60
30	15	50

$$I.Q. = \frac{M.A. \times 100}{C.A.}$$

In fact, of course, people do not become mentally deficient at 20 and imbecile at 30, despite the fact that their M.A. stops increasing after the age of 15. Therefore an adjustment has to be made in the C.A. over the age of 15 when calculating I.Q.s. Another difficulty encountered in this calculation occurs with the bright child of 15 or so. If, at the age of 5 this child had an M.A. of 7, then his I.Q. would be 140. Since, as we have seen I.Q. remains fairly constant, it follows that at the age of 15 such a child would have a theoretical M.A. of 21. This means very little since mental age is defined as the performance of the average person of a given age, and the average person of 21 performs no better than the average person of 15.

Because of difficulties such as these the concept of " mental age " has largely fallen into disuse and I.Q.s are now calculated directly from the test score by finding out the average score obtained by people at various ages. I.Q.s are then based on the distribution of scores on either side of the mean score at each given age.

Inheritance of Intelligence

It has long been recognised that clever parents tend to have clever children, and dull parents dull children. Children of the same family tend to have similar intelligences. Now it is difficult to persuade parents to submit to having their intelligences tested, so it is more usual to measure the I.Q.s of children of fathers whose occupations are known, making the assumption that it needs more brains, for example, to be a doctor than to sweep the streets. It can also be assumed that brighter men tend to choose brighter wives, and duller men to marry

duller wives. The following table gives the mean I.Q.s of children of
fathers of various occupational groups:

Table 2

Occupation of Father	Mean I.Q. of Children
Professional	116
Semi-professional and managerial	112
Clerical, skilled trades, retail business	107
Semi-skilled, minor clerical and business	105
Slightly skilled	98
Rural and day labourers	95

Another source of evidence on the inheritance of intellectual ability
comes from studies of identical twins. Before discussing the next
table, however, a word must be said about the meaning of the term
" correlation ".

A *correlation* is a statistical measure for assessing the degree of association between two variables. If a class of children in a school were given
two tests, one English and the other arithmetic, and it was found that
children who did well in one test also did well in the other, and those
who did badly in one test also did badly in the other, then these two
tests would be said to be highly " correlated ". That is to say the two
arrays of scores would be closely associated.   Correlations are so
calculated that a perfect correlation would be unity, and no correlation
at all would be zero. A good correlation would be about 0.7 or 0.8
and a poor one about 0.2 or 0.3. In the following table we see that
identical twins have the highest correlation between their I.Q.
measures, and that the size of the correlation falls off as the degree of
blood relationship diminishes.

Table 3
Correlations of I.Q.s of Variously Related Children *

Identical twins	0.90
Fraternal twins, like sex	0.70
Fraternal twins, unlike sex	0.60
Siblings	0.50
First cousins	0.20
Unrelated children	0.00

* These are average correlations obtained with verbal group-tests of intelligence.

This supports the theory that hereditary factors largely decide intelligence. If we look at the next table, we see that the size of the correlation is to some extent affected by the environment, since it is higher for twins reared together than it is for twins reared apart.

Table 4

Correlations of Three Measures for Related and Unrelated Children †

	Height	Intelligence	General Attainments
Identical twins reared together	0.96	0.92	0.89
Identical twins reared apart	0.94	0.85	0.63
Siblings reared together	0.50	0.49	0.81
Unrelated children reared together	0.00	0.25	0.54

Moreover the correlation for twins reared apart is higher for height than it is for intelligence, but lower for attainments than it is for intelligence. It will also be seen that for siblings reared together, the correlation for attainments is actually higher than for twins reared apart, but not as high as for twins reared together. It would seem that environment has a marked effect on educational attainments, as might be expected, less effect on intelligence, and least of all on height. The correlation for the height of twins is the same whether they are reared together or apart.

Clinical Applications of Intelligence Tests

The way a patient is handled by the doctor or nurse should bear some relation to his intellectual level, particularly with respect to explanations given to him about what is wrong with him and about what his treatment is to be. If complicated treatments are to be used involving the patient's close co-operation, especially in such matters as diet, then a knowledge, however approximate, of the patient's intellectual level is of the first importance.

A knowledge of the changes in the pattern of abilities with age is also clearly relevant, and has a direct bearing on the management of children and old people.

In making some sort of estimate of a patient's intellectual level in the ward or clinic, important evidence is gained from what he says

† These figures are quoted from surveys carried out by Burt and his co-workers. The total number of pairs of identical twins reared apart amounted to 48.

and how he says it. The range and complexity of his vocabulary is important, and how clearly he manages to convey the meaning of what he wants to say. In assessing this, an account will obviously have to be taken of the patient's age, and to some extent his social class. There is increasing evidence now that people from some working-class environments never attain the sophisticated use of words achieved by middle-class people, although they may be just as intelligent. Thus quite difficult concepts can be understood by such people, as long as simple terms are used; and their own inability to express themselves in sophisticated language does not necessarily reflect a lack of intelligence. Educational history and present occupation are both useful guides to a person's intellectual capacity.

Tests designed to assess innate capacity separately from acquired knowledge have an important clinical use. When a patient suffers from brain damage or from any condition which leads to intellectual deterioration, it is usually found that the sort of test which assesses innate capacity has been affected much more than the sort designed to assess acquired knowledge. Brain-damaged people who do quite badly on tests for innate capacity may still continue to give good performances on a test for acquired knowledge, such as a vocabulary test. A person who scores above average in the innate capacity test will also score above average in the vocabulary test provided he has had normal educational opportunities. If such a person becomes intellectually impaired for any reason, his innate capacity score is likely to drop, while his vocabulary remains above average as before. There are, of course, difficulties in this type of assessment. Take, for example, a man who is clever and scores above average on innate capacity tests, but who has had little opportunity or inclination to acquire a comparable vocabulary. His school attendance may have been erratic, or he may have come from a home environment in which a sophisticated use of words was not possible. In this case the vocabulary level may be only average or even below. If such a person suffers brain damage, his innate capacity score will drop and may now match his lower vocabulary score. On testing there will now be no discrepancy between the two kinds of test, and his deterioration may not be suspected. This actually happened in one case, and it was only when reference was made to the patient's occupation that his very superior work record revealed his high pre-morbid intellectual level. This particular man was an alcoholic, and when he was re-tested after a somewhat lengthy treatment, he scored highly on the intellectual capacity tests, but still only produced an average score on the vocabulary test. Some forms of intellectual deterioration do, of course, affect performance on vocabulary tests, but if this is so they produce a much more marked and serious deterioration of innate capacity tests, so that the discrepancy between the two remains.

Intelligence is an important part of the patient's personality, it helps to make him what he is, and to modify the way he reacts to medical treatment. A knowledge of this aspect of the patient is an important factor in deciding the best way of managing him through his illness and convalescence.

SELECTED BIBLIOGRAPHY

Intelligence and Attainment Tests. Vernon, P. E. 1960. University of London Press.

Chapter 6

PHYSIOLOGICAL ASPECTS OF PERCEPTION, SPEECH AND MEMORY

It has now been accepted that most psychological phenomena have a basis in the physiological functioning of the central nervous system (C.N.S.). Until the end of the nineteenth century no real progress was made in understanding the nature of these physiological processes. Even in this century, many of the ideas put forward have been speculative and based on little concrete experimental or clinical evidence. However, in the last decade more data have come to light, and it is now possible to paint a tentative picture of certain aspects of this problem, and to feel more confident that its general outline will be recognisable in ten years' time.

The psychological processes of perceiving, speaking and remembering are dependent upon the normal functioning of the whole of the C.N.S., and also of certain special parts of it. It is with these special parts and their relationship to psychological phenomena that this chapter will be concerned.

Physiological Aspects of Perception

As we saw in Chapter 2, perception is the " awareness of objects, qualities or relations which ensues directly upon the stimulation of sense organs ". One of the most important psychological aspects of perception is its selectivity. Why a person becomes aware of certain stimuli acting upon him and remains unaware of other sensory stimuli is one of the fundamental problems of both the psychology and physiology of perception. We say that the person *attends to* certain stimuli or that his *attention* is focused upon certain stimuli. No living organism responds equally to the whole barrage of sensory stimuli bombarding it at any given moment, it responds by focusing selectively on one group of stimuli and largely neglecting the rest. Later the focus of attention may shift to another group of stimuli. Two parts of the C.N.S. are particularly important in enabling this selective focusing to take place: firstly the *cerebral cortex* and secondly the *reticular system* of the brain stem (see Chapter 13).

The Cerebral Cortex and Selectivity of Attention

In normal human beings a stimulus such as a pin prick applied to the hand, produces an electrical disturbance over the scalp which can be detected by a sensitive apparatus know as an electro-encephalo-graph (E.E.G.).*

In animals stimulation of the cerebral cortex in the region of the sensory cortex can suppress or modify nerve impulses travelling from the limbs, trunk or head of the animal. Impulses must descend from the cortex and affect the sensory impulses as they travel from the periphery to the cerebral cortex. In one series of experiments performed on rats a volley of sensory impulses was produced by stimulating the peripheral sense organs. The nervous impulses were detected travelling up the posterior columns, synapsing in the cuneate nucleus, travelling to the thalamus and ending up in the sensory cortex. As soon as stimulation was applied to the cortex of the same hemisphere in the region of the sensory cortex the nerve impulses could no longer be detected past the cuneate nucleus. A true inhibiting effect had been produced on the post-synaptic impulses. The C.N.S. was thus selecting which impulses reached the cortex and which did not.

Considerable anatomical evidence is accumulating showing that real pathways exist by which the cortex exerts its influence on the afferent impulses. Destruction of various parts of the sensory cortex is followed by degeneration of the fibres terminating in the cuneate nucleus.

The effect of presenting to an animal two groups of stimuli at the same time has been studied in cats by Hernandez-Peon. He studied the effect of competitive groups of stimuli on the electrical responses in the cortex. First of all he presented a flashing light to the animal and recorded the magnitude of the electrical response in the occipital cortex. Next he presented a fish for the animal to smell and lastly he presented the flashing light and the fish together. When the two stimuli were presented together the electrical response in the occipital cortex was almost abolished.

The fundamental difficulty involved in interpreting experimental work of this nature is that we do not know the relationship between electrical activity in the cortex and actual perception of the stimuli recorded. We can probably assume without being too inaccurate that when the electrical activity in the cortex due to sensory impulses is almost completely suppressed the focus of attention is elsewhere. In Hernandez-Peon's experiments the cat was focusing its attention on the flashing light to begin with, but noticed only the fish when the two were presented together.

Perception by the cortex is selective and nerve impulses descending from the cerebral cortex modify the amount and type of sensory data received by the cortex itself.

---

* See Glossary.

The Reticular Formation and Selectivity of Perception

The reticular formation is a mass of nerve cells and fibres situated in the brain stem and having intimate connection with the cerebral hemispheres. It has two important properties that concern us in our study of perception. Stimulation of certain parts in the sleeping animal will produce a state of wakefulness and alertness. Stimulation of other parts can produce drowsiness (see Chapter 13).

The degree to which a person is aware of any incoming signal will depend upon the activity of the reticular system. When the activity of the system falls below a certain level the person concerned becomes unaware of the afferent impulses. If a person who is deeply asleep is pricked on his hand, that hand will tend to move away from the noxious stimulus showing that the sensory pathways are intact. He will not be aware of that stimulus, that is he will not have perceived it because his cerebral cortex has not been kept in a waking state by his reticular system. As soon as he is woken up perception of the stimulus takes place.

The reticular system not only plays this general role in the control of the ability of the cerebral cortex to become aware of afferent impulses, it also has a particular role to play in the " filtering out " of sensory information. Stimulation of certain parts of the reticular system reduces the quantity of afferent impulses reaching cortical level. It seems to protect the cortex from becoming overloaded with the reception of sensory impulses from all over the body. This function of the reticular system may be directed by the cortex itself.

The Cerebral Cortex and the Perception of Shapes and Qualities

Perception involves at least two operations. These are best illustrated by the example of tactile perception. In the recognition of objects by touch, properties such as the size, shape and consistency are first noted and then the meaning of these properties is inferred. A match box placed in the hand of a blindfolded man is perceived as being rectangular with one rough surface, and in the light of past experience, it is recognised as a match box. These operations of tactile perception are dependent upon the normal functioning of part of the parietal lobe. In a person who has damage to either parietal lobe in the region of the sensory cortex, the ability to experience crude sensations such as light touch, deep touch, pain or temperature may not be grossly impaired, but his ability to recognise objects by touch may be completely absent. Although he may be able to tell that he is being touched with the blunt or sharp end of a pin, he will be unable to recognise common objects such as a pencil or comb placed in his hand. As soon as he looks at the object he will recognise it immediately.

Tactile Perception as opposed to *tactile sensation* depends upon having certain parts of the parietal lobe in the region of the post central gyrus functioning normally.

The underlying physiological basis of visual perception is even more complex and certainly not fully understood to this day. Munk in 1877 performed a series of experiments on dogs which threw some light on

Left Cerebral Hemisphere

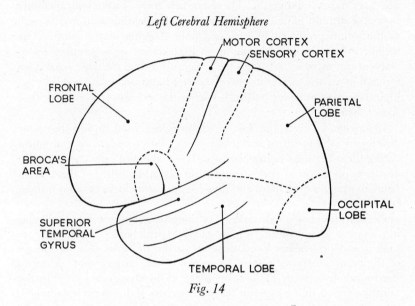

Fig. 14

the subject. He removed large areas of the cerebral cortex in the region of the occipital lobes and then studied the dogs' behaviour in some detail. As far as he could observe, they avoided objects in their way, but they did not recognise their owner and appeared unmoved by objects such as a whip or flaming torch that normally would have a significant meaning for them. When he later removed even more of the occipital cortex he found they became completely blind. In Munk's experiments the ability of the dogs to perceive the size and shape of the objects was only slightly impaired, it was the recognition of the nature and meaning of the objects that had completely disappeared. This work has since been confirmed.

Since Munk's experiments comparable cases in human beings have come to light. These cases are always very complex and difficult to interpret but there is no doubt that in human beings visual perception does depend upon the normal functioning of the occipital lobes.

Physiological Aspects of Speech

Human beings as they grow and develop attach meanings to the various sets of sensory stimuli that they encounter. As soon as a set of stimuli acquires a meaning it becomes a signal to the person concerned. To a man driving a motor car a particular type of red light means " stop ", to a criminal on the run from the police the bark of a dog may mean " danger ". There are two ways of attaching meaning to sets of stimuli. The first is by associating meaning with events such as the sound produced by an open door banging in the wind. The second is by associating meaning in accordance with accepted social conventions as when a " keep left " sign on a dual carriage road is an indication to the driver to take the left-hand roadway and not an invitation to change his politics. It is to the second type of signal that speech belongs.

Language involves the use of auditory or visual stimuli that have developed as a result of social agreement into a means of communicating ideas between human beings. It involves not only the reception and interpretation of these stimuli, but also the ability of the human being to manufacture them and thus communicate ideas to other human beings.

Certain psychological aspects of language will be of particular importance when considering its physiological basis. The ability to understand the spoken word depends in the first place on the power of the central nervous system to recognise the pattern and nature of the sounds produced. This takes place at an elementary level in the auditory cortex in the superior temporal gyrus. If this gyrus is damaged, especially on both sides, the pattern and pitch of the sounds may not be fully recognised and the comprehension of spoken language is lost. In this case, however, written language would be little affected. The reverse applies if the occipital lobe is damaged. In this, especially if both lobes are damaged, visual perception will be impaired and the ability to understand the written word will be lost (see diagram on p. 59).

Very little is known about the areas of the cortex specifically involved in the appreciation of the spoken word as opposed to auditory perception generally. This receptive area is situated in the dominant hemisphere: that is, the left hemisphere in right-handed people. It tends to have rather ill-defined boundaries, but in general it is situated in the posterior part of the superior temporal gyrus and adjacent areas in the parietal lobe. Damage to this region produces loss of comprehension for speech without severe loss of ordinary auditory perception. Although people who have damage to this area cannot understand much of what is said to them, they appear to be able to recognise tunes in music. As verbal comprehension is lost it is extremely difficult to assess these people and the interpretation of the results of tests is difficult and uncertain.

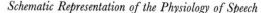

Schematic Representation of the Physiology of Speech

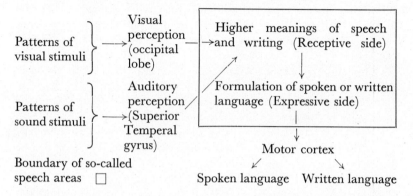

The formulation of both written and spoken language seems to depend upon an area situated at the posterior end of the left inferior frontal gyrus, usually called Broca's area. Damage to this area produces difficulty in naming objects or expressing ideas in sentences. Again, as in the case of patients with comprehension difficulties, the interpretation of tests with patients with expressive difficulties is extremely difficult.

After the formulation of language has taken place it is transformed into actual speech or writing by means of the motor cortex and the normal pyramidal pathways.

The Physical Basis of Memory

Spontaneous or Artificially Produced Memories

Physicians and psychiatrists have for many years been aware that damage to the region of the temporal lobe can lead to disturbances of memory.

Penfield and his colleagues studied patients who were undergoing neurosurgical operations, under local anaesthetics. The brain had to be exposed for technical reasons and Penfield took the opportunity of stimulating various parts of the temporal lobe. He found that stimulation would produce spontaneously recalled memories. If he repeated the stimulation he produced the same or occasionally a slightly different memory. These memories were very vivid and often accompanied by spontaneous emotions associated with the recalled event. Such memories included images of hearing, sight, taste, and smell. The same sort of spontaneous recall is seen occasionally in a condition known as temporal lobe epilepsy. In this a small area of damage in the temporal lobe acts as an irritating focus stimulating the area around it. The writer recalls a patient who was a married woman in her late thirties. Periodically she would feel peculiar and start to experience an event that occurred in her childhood. She described it as a dream-like state in which she was actually experiencing the dream but at the same time remaining aware of her surroundings. She felt her-self transported back to her childhood and was playing a game of hide and seek with her younger sister. In the middle of the game she could hear her mother calling her and her sister in for tea.

Bickford and his colleagues have shown that not only can memories be recalled by stimulation of the temporal lobe but they can also be lost. Stimulation of the posterior part of the temporal lobe can on occasion produce loss of memory for several days prior to the event. The actual loss of memory is related to the duration of stimulation and recovery occurs in a few minutes or hours.

Pathological Loss of Retention of Memories

In psychiatric practice an interesting condition is seen which sheds considerable light on various aspects of memory function. This condition is known as *Korsakov's syndrome*. In this condition the patient remembers most of the events that happened before the condition arose but virtually nothing that happened afterwards. He may have been in hospital for many years but will not be able to recall when he came in, the name of the doctor or sister in charge nor indeed what he had for breakfast nor what he saw on the television the previous evening. He fills in the gap in his memory by making up details and happenings. His recall for events in his childhood or indeed anything before the onset of the condition is moderately good.

A study of the areas of the brain consistently affected by this condition shows that it is mainly confined to the diencephalon. The peri-ventricular grey matter around the third ventricle with occasional caudal extension into the peri-acqueductal region of the mid-brain is consistently damaged. The mammillary bodies are also always affected and sometimes grossly so. A similar syndrome can occur when the so-called Limbic System is damaged. This system includes the amygdala, hippocampus, hippocampal gyrus, cingulate gyrus and parts of the diencephalon. The symptoms are most marked when the hippocampus is involved.

All the evidence so far discussed suggests that there are three regions of the brain mainly concerned in the function of memory:

1. The temporal lobe.
2. The mammillary bodies and the region around the third ventricle.
3. The limbic system.

All these regions are linked together by tracts and probably function as a whole. These areas are concerned in impression and reproduction (see

Diencephalon

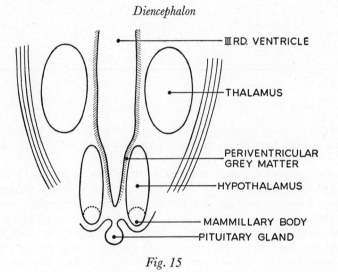

Fig. 15

Chapter 4). There is nothing to suggest that these structures themselves act as storehouses of memory, indeed the evidence is to the contrary, as remote memories may be preserved even when these structures are destroyed.

The Retention of Remote Memories

As was noted in Chapter 4, there is a striking difference between the relative ease with which recent memories can be removed and the difficulty in disturbing remote memories. A study of the psychological effects of head injury on memory illustrates this difference.

When a person is knocked unconscious for even a limited period of time he may not be able to remember events leading up to the injury. This is called *retrograde amnesia* and may extend for a few hours or few days before the injury.

After the patient regains consciousness a much longer period occurs when he is unable to remember events that happen to him, this is called *anterograde amnesia* and may last for several hours, days or weeks. It is only the patient's recent memory that is affected. He can recall events in his childhood or recognise his family and friends without much difficulty, but during the period of anterograde amnesia he may not remember having been visited by them. Patients suffering from head injury have been known to complain bitterly that nobody comes to visit them although they have in fact been visited a few hours previously.

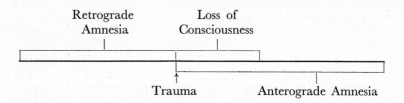

This resistance of remote memories to physical disturbances of the brain is even better seen in a common treatment used in psychiatric practice. Patients suffering from severe and persistent depression are treated by giving them an artificial fit. This is known as electro-convulsive therapy (E.C.T.).* A small current is passed through the frontal lobes for perhaps one second and when the patient goes into the fit the normal electrical activity of the whole brain disappears and is replaced by grossly irregular and violent electrical fluctuations. After the fit is over and the patient regains consciousness there is occasionally a retrograde amnesia lasting a few minutes but remote memories are hardly affected at all.

This difference between the vulnerability of recent and remote memories to loss as a result of physiological disturbances to the brain was discussed in Chapter 4 in terms of " consolidation ", when it was suggested that memories become fixed or consolidated in the course of time and thus become resistant to loss. Recent work has suggested that only actual chemical changes in the neurones themselves would be likely to survive the rather gross physiological disturbances associated with concussion or E.C.T. Such chemical changes are discussed in the next section.

The Molecular Basis of Memories

The evidence for memories being stored by molecular changes in the protein structure of cells is fairly strong in very primitive animals. James

---

* See Glossary.

McConnell and his colleagues have conducted a series of experiments with primitive flat worms called planarians. These flatworms are bilaterally symmetrical, have a rudimentary central nervous system consisting of a group of semi-specialised cells, and have a definite head end which appears to control the rest of the body. When they are

Reactions of Planarian Flat Worm

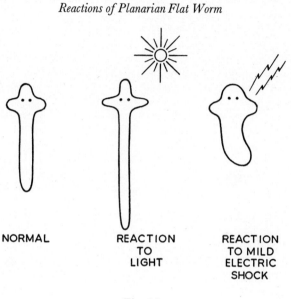

| NORMAL | REACTION TO LIGHT | REACTION TO MILD ELECTRIC SHOCK |

Fig. 16

placed in a bright light these worms stretch themselves and when given a mild electric shock they contract (Fig. 16). By shining the bright light several seconds before the mild electric shock these animals can be conditioned in the classical sense of the word to contract to the bright light (see Chapter 4). It takes approximately a hundred trials before the new response is fully learned.

McConnell trained planarians to contract on being exposed to a bright light. He then cut the worms in two and allowed the " head end " to grow a new tail and the " tail end " to grow a new head. Both of these new worms responded to a bright light by contracting. In other words both the " head end " and the " tail end " had retained the original memory trace. McConnell's next series of experiments yielded an even more incredible result. Again he trained a group of planarians to respond by contracting to a bright light. He then chopped them up into minute pieces and fed them to untrained worms. A high proportion of these worms showed the conditioned response. The conclusion was unavoidable that some complex chemical substance had passed from the trained to the untrained worms.

It is known that genetic information is stored by means of coding it on to the complex polynucleotide desoxyribonucleic acid (D.N.A.). The code is built into the structure mainly by means of changes in the sequence and nature of the nitrogenous bases attached to the chains. The hypothesis was put forward that memory traces may be coded in a similar way on to the related polynucleotide ribonucleic acid (R.N.A.). Corning and his colleagues set out to test this hypothesis. They trained planarians to respond to strong light by contracting as in the previous experiments. Again they cut them into two pieces but this time left them to regenerate in a solution of ribonuclease. This enzyme destroys R.N.A. if it can get at it in the cell but usually in the living organism it just prevents new R.N.A. being formed. They found that the new worms which developed from the " head end " of the original planarian retained some of the original learning. The new worms which regenerated from the " tail end " retained no learning at all. As regeneration of a " new head " involved the production of new R.N.A. derived from the R.N.A. of the tail this is the result that would be expected if R.N.A. contained the memory traces.

There is thus strong evidence that coding on to the R.N.A. molecule is one of the methods of storing memory in living animal tissues. It is more than possible that remote memories in the mammalian brain are stored in a similar way and experiments have been performed which would support this hypothesis.

SELECTED BIBLIOGRAPHY

1. *Recent Advances in Neurology and Neuropsychiatry.* 7th Edition. Ed. Russell Brain. 1962. London: Churchill.
   This chapter has, in part, been based on data given in the first two chapters of this book.
2. *The Parietal Lobes.* McDonald Critchley. 1953. London: Arnold.
3. *Scientific American.* February 1963. pp. 55–62.
   " A study of remembering in planarians." J. B. Best.

Chapter 7

MOTIVATION

Determinism and Free-will

One of the central problems of psychology is that of motivation. Why do people behave as they do? What makes them tick? What makes one man behave in one way in a given situation and another man behave quite differently?

In order to try and answer some of these questions, psychologists have used a number of explanatory concepts such as *need*, *drive*, *motive* and *instinct*. These are overlapping terms which are to some extent interchangeable and are, in any case, used differently by different authorities. However, there is now general agreement that all behaviour is motivated: we behave as we do because we have a motive for doing so, although such a motive may be an unconscious one. Some psychologists even go so far as to assert that our behaviour is totally controlled by hereditary and environmental factors so that there is in fact no choice of action and no such thing as free-will. According to this point of view we are at the mercy of our needs and drives, and respond automatically to such stimuli as impinge on our sense organs. If we knew enough, such psychologists say, about an individual's inherited characteristics and about the environmental influences to which he had been subjected up to date, we could predict precisely what he would do in any given circumstances. Stated in this bald way this seems nonsensical. It would certainly flatly contradict our own experience and the opinion of Society which clearly holds that all normal people are responsible for their actions. A magistrate would be unsympathetic to any plea that a defendant could not help breaking the law since he was the victim of his heredity and environment.

Nevertheless we are creatures of habit, and it is quite possible to predict within fairly broad limits what people are likely to be doing at certain times of the day, and even how they are likely to react in certain circumstances. As one American psychologist once observed, although many instances have occurred in which a train has failed to reach its destination because the engine has broken down, there are no occasions on record when a train has been delayed because the engine driver wanted to get down and pick daisies. In this sense men are more predictable than machines.

65

These questions are of much more than mere academic interest. The natural sciences have tended to assume a strict causal connection between present events and those that have gone before. Physical events that are happening now, happen in this way because of certain physical events that have preceded them. Chemistry and physics assume this without question. Acids and bases mix to form salts and water because this is the way things happen. There is no question of " motive " here. The acid is not supposed to want to become part of a salt, and does not seek out the base with which to mix to achieve this end.

Motives imply future goals. We behave in certain ways because we wish to achieve certain ends. This way of looking at things has been given the name " teleological" as opposed to the " deterministic " view of natural science. Now some psychologists have insisted on applying deterministic ways of thinking to human motivation, and to argue that we only wish for certain future goals and appear to strive for them because of past events and experiences. In this way they attempt to force the facts of human experience into the classical deterministic mould inherited from natural science. As we have already pointed out, this does not fit the facts of human experience. This is not what seems to happen. A doctor treats his patients in teleological terms. He gives the patient this or that treatment because he wants the patient to get better, not because he was born and trained to react in this sort of way in these particular circumstances.

Feelings and Emotion

Before we go on to discuss various kinds of human needs, it is necessary first to say something about feelings and emotion. Most experiences that we have are more or less pleasurably toned. Some sights, sounds, tastes and smells are pleasant and some unpleasant, some neither one nor the other. As we saw in Chapter 4, we tend to remember or learn those actions which are pleasant or lead to pleasant experiences, and forget or at least avoid those actions which are unpleasant or lead to unpleasant experiences. Thus the feeling-tone of an experience is an important factor in whether or not we remember it or repeat it later when we have the opportunity.

As we shall see later in this chapter, men have a number of clearly defined needs, some physiological and some psychological. If these needs are not met men experience a state of tension which is distressing. This state of tension is such that it tends to make men act in order to reduce it. If a man is denied food he gets hungry, this is unpleasant and he seeks food in order to reduce the unpleasant feeling. Or if he is in a position of danger he has a need to escape and feels a state of tension if he cannot do so. This particular state of tension is known as fear. If he meets an enemy he may feel a need to assault him, and if frustrated from doing so will feel tension which in this case is anger. McDougall made a list of these particular sets of complicated needs in specific situations, and pointed out that there was a particular feeling associated with the tension aroused if the need was not met. This feeling is called an *emotion* because it moves us to action.

Need	Emotion aroused if need not satisfied, and diminished by such satisfaction
To escape from danger	Fear
To attack an enemy	Rage
To repulse a loathsome object	Disgust
To protect a child	Tenderness
To have sexual intercourse	Lust
To discover the unknown	Curiosity

McDougall produced a list of some fourteen " instincts " or complex needs as we have termed them, which included some rather vague ones such as " appeal," " assertion," " acquisition " and " construction ". With these it is more difficult to discern any recognisable emotion that is experienced if such needs are not met.

When our needs are satisfied, then these particular emotions disappear: we cease to be frightened when we escape from danger, we cease to be angry once we have assaulted our enemy, we cease to be disgusted once we have disposed of the loathsome object. But during and after the satisfaction of these needs, these emotions may be replaced by other kinds of emotion. Thus fear may turn to joy when a danger is averted, or disgust to relief when the object of disgust is repelled, or curiosity to contentment when we have discovered the unknown. As we shall see in Chapter 10, these two classes of emotion have rather different physiological concomitants. It is convenient to refer to emotions which arise from unsatisfied needs as *drive emotions*, and those which arise as the need is being satisfied, or as a result of satisfaction as *reward emotions*. The former impel or drive us to take action and are in the main unpleasant emotions; and the latter are pleasant and reward us for having taken action which has been successful in meeting the need.

McDougall's system of instincts are rather out of fashion now, and the system we discuss in the next sections is more convincing. However, McDougall was sound when he pointed out that emotion is intimately connected with the satisfaction of needs. We must now turn to a discussion of how these needs can be classified. We shall do this by speaking about *Deficit Motives* and *Growth Motives*.

Deficit Motives

First of all there are some quite obvious *physiological needs*. These are air, water, food, rest and sleep, elimination, physical exercise and sensory stimulation, warmth and shelter.

Men become ill and in the end may die if these basic needs are not met. As we have seen, if they are not met men experience a state of tension which is distressing. In some cases, this tension, especially with the more complex needs to be discussed later, amounts to a clearly recognisable emotion. This provides the *drive* or impulsion to the sort of behaviour which might be expected to lead to a reduction of such tension or emotional state (drive emotion). In turn, this reduction is pleasurable and rewarding, and the emotion may turn to a pleasurable one (reward emotion). This rewarding of the successful tension reducing behaviour tends to lead to a repetition of it when the need occurs again at a later date. As we saw when we were discussing instrumental learning in Chapter 4, the hungry rat presses a lever and is rewarded with food. This reduces the tension created by the unsatisfied need, and is, we suppose, pleasurable to the rat. When he is hungry again he tends to repeat his lever pressing because it gave him pleasure before. There are other deficit motives which are not so clearly physiological, but which are equally important for the survival of the animal or human being. They are sometimes called *psychological needs*, and include the need to feel secure from danger, to love and be loved, and to achieve self-esteem and the esteem of others. All these needs impel people to take action of one sort or another, which they think will lead to the satisfaction of the need in question.

As an example we can take that of a man arrested on some criminal charge for which, if he is found guilty, he may have to serve a prison sentence. We can assume he is allowed bail. He will feel frightened at the prospect of having to go to prison. Fear is an emotional state arising from his unsatisfied need to escape from the danger of receiving a prison sentence. He takes energetic action by instructing his solicitor to engage the best available counsel, and he sells out some stocks and shares to pay the expected bills. He remains frightened, and this fear impels him to any further action he can usefully take. In fact he is innocent of the charge, and his counsel manages to secure a judgment in his favour with costs. Immediately his fear turns to joy. His need to escape has been met, and he experiences a rewarding emotion. It is not unlikely therefore that if he were to find himself in a similar position in the future, he might instruct the same solicitor and barrister.

Growth Motives

If these basic deficit motives are acted on, and the needs they serve are met (that is the person has adequate air, water, food, rest and sleep, elimination, warmth, exercise and sensory stimulation) if he also has had an opportunity to feel secure from danger, to love and to be loved, and to achieve self-esteem and to be esteemed, then it seems that he is now more free to adopt less self-centred motives. These are the *growth motives*. He is less obsessed by his basic needs so that he can reach out for wider goals less intimately concerned with himself. Maslow, who is the chief proponent of this way of thinking about motives, speaks of the need for self-actualisation. This is man's desire for self-fulfilment, for being the best that he can be, for actualising his potential. That such a need exists, and is powerful in people who have no more worries about their basic needs, seems increasingly clear as the standard of living rises, and the deficit needs are met in more and more people. Once we cease to have to worry about food, shelter, esteem, security and so on, we begin to reach out for the satisfaction of needs that before we never even realised we had. We begin to experience the need to know and to understand more of the world around us. If this need is not met we become bored and seek some sort of diversion, something to be interested in, curious about. Another such growth need is the aesthetic need; the craving for beauty in various forms, pictures, music, scenes of natural beauty and so on. Personal relationships too, take on a different quality once the deficit needs are replaced by the growth needs. If our basic need to love and to be loved has not been satisfied, then we form relationships with others with a view to meeting that need. Like children, we need something from others. If these basic deficit needs have been met, then we form relationships with other people not for what we can get out of it for ourselves, but because of our interest in the other person in and for themselves.

It will be seen that this has a direct bearing on medicine, since the doctor will clearly do his work best when his relationship with his patient is of the kind based on growth motives rather than on deficit motives. If he treats his patients because he needs to bolster up his self-esteem, or needs to win the regard of his patients, or even because he feels insecure and may be short of money; then he is not so likely to be as successful as when his treatment arises from growth motives: his need to be as good a doctor as he can, his need to understand as much as possible about medicine, or his interest in his patients in and for themselves.

Hierarchy of Motives

It will be obvious from what has gone before that some motives or needs are more potent and compelling than others. As we have seen, some are not operative to any extent until more basic needs are met. Thus it is that the physiological motives are the most potent. A man deprived of air will forget all else in his fight to satisfy his air-hunger. He will forget thirst, cold or tiredness. Even more will he forget love or esteem needs. When the physiological needs have been met, the individual is ready to realise and seek to meet his psychological needs. Only when he has satisfied his needs for security, love, and esteem, will he be ready to realise and meet the growth needs of curiosity, aesthetic appreciation and self-fulfilment. Thus the motives are arranged in a hierarchy. McKellar quotes an interesting personal example of how needs can arrange themselves in such a hierarchy.

> " Six tired, cold and hungry men, . . . were making their way across a glacier late one evening. . . . . Though exceedingly cold, tired and hungry, the men did not pitch their tent in an exposed part of the glacier nor stop for a meal nor lie down to sleep. Instead they sought a place of safety before they attempted to satisfy their other nevertheless pressing needs. Once a safe and sheltered spot had been reached behaviour was determined by motives, formerly less prepotent, which now became most influential. They pitched the tent and were thus able to obtain some degree of warmth. They then sat down inside the tent and had their meal. Finally, when the needs for safety, warmth, food and drink had been satisfied, they lay down to rest and to satisfy, last of all, the need for sleep."

It is interesting to note that in other circumstances the needs might have assumed a different order of importance. Very hungry men will risk danger to get food, or very sleepy men will fall asleep in cold and exposed places. In the example given, the men had food with them, and could wait until they were safe and warm before they ate it, and they were not too sleepy to attend to other things first.

Motivation and Learning

The motives we have been discussing have all been innate: that is men do not have to be taught to fight for air, seek food and drink, warmth and shelter, exercise or rest. Neither do they have to be taught to seek love, esteem or security. These seem to be basic needs, which, if they are not met, lead to the illness or death of the individual. We make no distinction here between mental and physical illness, their interdependence is sufficiently stressed throughout the book. Men can, and certainly do, learn to adopt different methods of satisfying their needs. A man who has learnt that eating steak and chips is a pleasurable way of satisfying his hunger, may meet this need in this way as often as he can. The insistence of the Englishman abroad for bacon and eggs at breakfast, amusing to the Continental, also testifies to the powerful nature of habit formation in need reduction.

Allport has commented on the great differences in human behaviour, pointing out that the comparatively meagre store of innate needs or motives could not possibly account for this wide variability in behaviour. He has introduced a concept which he has called the *functional autonomy of motives*, in which he suggests that sometimes means become ends in themselves. A man may go to sea in order to earn a living, but develops a passion for the sea which far outlasts the original motive which sent him there. A craftsman may continue to produce fine work although it no longer pays him financially. Thus new motives can be acquired, old ones transformed, habits formed and broken. Motives can also, of course, conflict. Such conflicting motives can both be conscious, or one or both can be unconscious, and man has a number of ways of dealing with such conflicting motives. These are dealt with in Chapter 8.

Unconscious Motives

Many motives giving rise to an individual's behaviour may not only be hidden to the observer, but may also be unsuspected by the person himself. For example a man might be very careful about spending money, and will walk rather than pay a threepenny bus fare, or he will invariably choose the cheapest dish on the menu. What might his motive be? If we asked him he might say he was saving up for a new television set. This could be a motive. But we might enquire further and say " Why buy a new one when your old one works well enough? " He might give a number of reasons: better definition, larger screen, better sound reproduction. If we pressed him still further, he might admit that the Jones next door had recently bought a new set, much superior to his, and that he wanted to keep up with them. So his more basic motive might be the need to bolster up his self-esteem and to gain social prestige. On further enquiry we might discover that this man desperately needed other people's affection, and that he thought people were more likely to be friendly with him if he could win their social approval and admiration. This need for affection might have arisen in a childhood which was rather grim and affectionless. Thus these deeper needs for prestige, approval or affection might manifest themselves in this man's careful expenditure of money, and all he might be conscious of when he walked to work was his desire to save up for the new television set.

SELECTED BIBLIOGRAPHY

1. *A Text Book of Human Psychology.* McKellar, P. 1952. London: Cohen and West. Chapters 2, 3 and 4.
2. *Introduction to Psychology.* Morgan, C. T. 1956. New York: McGraw-Hill. Chapters 3 and 4.
3. *Learning Theory and Behaviour.* Mowrer, O. H. 1960. New York: Wiley. This is a difficult book, but contains evidence for some of the ideas in this chapter.
4. *Motivation and Personality.* Maslow, A. H. 1954. New York: Harper. Chapter 5.

Chapter 8

NORMAL CONFLICT, FRUSTRATION AND REACTION TO STRESS

As we saw in the last chapter many motives that people have may not be apparent to the outside observer and in the case of some of these motives the person himself may not be fully aware of them. Writers and philosophers have known that the real motives behind people's actions may not be the ones consciously expressed. Some artists have known intuitively that motives strongly suppressed, the nature of which the person will not even admit to himself, can give rise to mental and physical disturbances. Shakespeare gives us a convincing (if fictitious) illustration of the effects of " hidden " painful memories and feelings in the case of Lady Macbeth's sleep-walking and fruitless hand-washing. She does not consciously feel remorse for instigating several terrible murders, but unconscious anxiety and guilt are obviously at work, disrupting her sleep and provoking her symbolically to wash away her sins.

Unconscious Motivation and the Rise of Psychoanalysis

It was not until the end of the nineteenth century that these phenomena were investigated from the clinical point of view. The physician who studied all these complex processes almost single-handed was Sigmund Freud and to understand the subject it is illuminating to know a little about the man himself.

As a schoolboy Freud was not particularly interested in medicine as such, he was more interested in studying and understanding how animals, human beings and societies worked. As at that time his main interest was science and humanism he felt that medicine would give him the sort of education he desired and in 1873 he entered Vienna University as a medical student. After a few years of study he was side tracked into doing research at the Institute of Physiology. This was mainly on the anatomy of the C.N.S. and as a consequence he did not graduate until he was 25. He was then very interested in neurology and chose to do his clinical work in a hospital that specialised in diseases of the brain. Gradually he became more and more fascinated by those " nervous conditions " for which there was no anatomical explanation. After a visit to Paris in 1885 during which he studied under Charcot his lifelong interest in the psychological causation of illness began. Charcot at that time was mainly interested in hysteria and hypnosis.

It was around that time that Freud learned of the use of hypnosis by a senior colleague of his in the treatment of hysteria. This colleague was Dr. Joseph Breuer. Breuer's original patient was a highly intelligent girl of 21. Over the previous two years she had suffered from recurrent disabling symptoms. Her right arm and leg and occasionally her left arm and leg would become paralysed, she would lose the ability to speak and periodically her ability to swallow fluids would diminish to such an extent that she would suffer from extreme thirst and would eat fruits to rehydrate herself. At other times her vision was affected and she would become confused. All these symptoms were impossible to account for on a physical basis, indeed such was their nature that only a diagnosis of hysteria was tenable. Breuer had noticed that during the periods of altered personality and confusion the patient would utter a few words that seemed to refer to events in the past. Under hypnosis he succeeded in getting the girl to remember the particular events that led up to each symptom in turn. When she remembered in what connections the symptoms arose and spoke about the events with feeling, the symptoms tended to disappear. When she was nursing her sick father her English " lady companion " had allowed the dog to drink out of the glass of water in the room. She was horrified and disgusted but at the time had said nothing. As soon as she had described the event under hypnosis and given vent to her feeling of disgust and anger she no longer had any difficulty in drinking.

Freud and Breuer were able to treat many patients suffering from hysteria by this method. Under hypnosis the patients were encouraged to recall particular experiences giving rise to specific symptoms and as soon as they had talked them out with emotion they obtained relief from the symptoms. The talking out of symptoms was called *abreaction* and the method itself was named *mental catharsis*.

Breuer soon gave up this form of treatment because one young girl he was treating developed a strong emotional attachment to him. Indeed she actually declared that she was in love with him. Breuer found this situation impossible to deal with professionally. Freud had in fact noticed similar phenomena but, putting a different interpretation on them, he did not find them so difficult to deal with. He noted that the patient's feeling towards the physician were a mixture of affection and hostility. During treatment the patient tended to become dependent and infantile. These feelings were part of the patient's emotional history which he or she could no longer recall, but which were re-activated by his new relationship with the physician. The emotions the patient had felt for his parents were simply transferred to the therapist. These positive and negative feelings that arose during treatment he called *transference*.

Gradually Freud was led to the abandonment of hypnosis as a method of treatment because he found that he could only hypnotise a small proportion of his patients and of these only a few sufficiently deeply for abreaction to take place. He therefore decided to give up hypnosis and to make mental catharsis independent of it. His object was to treat patients in a state of full consciousness. He had noticed that even when patients were under deep hypnosis and were told to forget everything that happened to them in that state they only seemed to have forgotten. With persistent questioning the lost memories always re-appeared. He had his patients relax on a couch, and instructed them to search their minds for the source of the trouble. When they failed Freud insisted that they knew it all and usually after strenuous efforts on the part of both physician and patient the required memories would come into the patient's consciousness. Freud came to the conclusion that these forgotten memories were prevented from reaching a conscious level by some force in the patient's mind. The force which originally had driven the emotionally charged memories into the unconscious mind he called *repression* and the act of using this force on the patient's part *resistance*. It was the task of the physician to help the patient to overcome this resistance and so obtain a better understanding of himself.

After a time Freud found that the more relaxed the patient was the easier it was for him to overcome his resistance without active intervention on the part of the physician. He had his patients relax mentally as well as physically on a couch and allow all their thoughts to come spontaneously into their minds. He insisted that they must verbalise everything that they thought of, no matter how trivial or embarrassing. This new method he called *free association*, and the form of treatment as a whole was called *psycho-analysis*. Freud found it particularly fruitful at the start of a course of free association to get the patient to remember a recent dream. He would then analyse the dream and encourage the patient to indulge in free association about all its items. During the course of psycho-analysis patients remembered facts about their early childhood in great detail. Some of these memories were charged with love, hate or fear about their relationships with their parents. They were not necessarily true happenings as on the few occasions when it proved possible to check their accuracy the events did not appear actually to have occurred. They were *fantasies:* hopes and fears from childhood that had lain dormant many years only to come to life again in the therapeutic situation.

Freud came to the conclusion that a large part of the mind was functioning at a level that was largely unconscious. By this he meant that the individual was mainly unaware of what was going on. He thought that this *unconscious* part of the mind consisted mainly of different motives, drives and needs. The most basic of these were the inherited biological drives, an important example being the sexual drive. He called the force behind these drives the *libido*. At a slightly more accessible level were the acquired motives. These motives were also in the unconscious and influenced behaviour in a way of which the patient was not aware. A married woman who loses her wedding ring was perhaps motivated by the desire to be single again. The most superficial level of the mind was that of the conscious mind, that is the thoughts, ideas and motives of which the person was fully aware. One of the underlying philosophical concepts which directed much of Freud's work was his belief in *psychic determinism*.* He held that all mental events have causes which derive from the unconscious. He did not believe that anybody could do or think anything as a result of chance. He thought that determinism applied as forcibly to psychological as it did to physical events (see Chapter 7). A further discussion on Freud's views on the psychological implications of dreams is to be found in Chapter 13.

Frustration and Conflict of Motives

What light have Freud's concepts thrown on our understanding of frustration? He found that unsatisfied unconscious needs gave rise to either anxiety or aggression. If a motive, need or drive does not reach its goal it is said to be *frustrated*. The frustrated motive does not need to be a biological drive to give rise to anxiety or aggression. Many of the acquired motives, such as the desire for status or for company can, when thwarted, give rise to tension. (Compare this formulation with the system of deficit and growth motives outlined in Chapter 7.)

Lewin, who studied the subject in great detail, came to the conclusion that there are only three basic ways by which a motive can be frustrated.

1. Difficulties in the subject's environment.
2. Limitations in the subject's abilities making the goal unobtainable.
3. Conflict within the personality between two or more motives.

Difficulties in the Environment

These difficulties are the simplest and most direct causes of frustration. The difficulties may be present because the goal is absent as in the

---

* See Glossary.

case of a man who after a long train journey arrives late at night in a city only to find all the cafés and restaurants closed. In children one sees this type of frustration frequently. A child out with its parents asks for a bar of chocolate but the parents in their wisdom think that it would spoil the child's appetite for its supper and so refuse the request. One has only to study the resulting reaction for a few minutes, seeing the child first go pale and then red, to realise that tension or anger are a direct result of the frustrated desire. Indeed many adults show similar reactions.

Limitations in the Subject's Ability

Here it is the limited nature of the subject's personality that makes the goal unobtainable. The goals the person sets himself are outside his ability to achieve. A newly qualified doctor may aspire to be a professor of medicine but unless he has the intellectual ability his desires will be frustrated. This sort of frustration can be illustrated by means of a type of diagram first used by Lewin. In the illustration (Diagram 1) below, M is the motive (in this case the desire of the doctor

$$\longrightarrow \quad \text{P} \quad \text{F} \quad \text{G}+$$
$$\text{M}$$

Diagram 1

to become professor of medicine), P is the person concerned (in this case the doctor). F is the frustrating factor (which is the doctor's intellectual limitations) and G is the eventual goal (the professorship of medicine). The motive has a direction towards the goal when this is positive.

Conflicts Within the Personality

Conflicts within the personality however are more important in clinical practice. These lead to neurotic reactions and minor mental illnesses. Lewin again delineated three variations of this type of conflct and we shall deal with each in turn.

Firstly there is the type of conflict in which the subject stands between two equally attractive goals. This is a very unstable situation for as the person moves to one of the goals, so the pull of the other fades

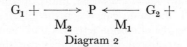

$$\text{G}_1 + \longrightarrow \text{P} \longleftarrow \text{G}_2 +$$
$$\text{M}_2 \qquad \text{M}_1$$

Diagram 2

and eventually the conflict is resolved, the subject moving to each goal in turn (see Diagram 2). A person after a long climb in the mountains may want both to eat and sleep. As he cannot do both together he usually eats first and then sleeps. Which he does first is determined by the hierarchy of needs discussed in Chapter 7. Similarly a student may desire both to stay in and work and to go out drinking with his friends. He may solve the conflict in this case by working for one hour before going out.

Secondly there is the more complicated conflict of a person who is faced with a goal that both attracts and repels him at the same time. This type of conflict can lead to great difficulties and unhappiness (see Diagram 3). A young man who has fallen in love may desire to get married (M_1) but at the same time he may fear that he is impotent (M_2). This type of conflict can only be resolved satisfactorily by removing the man's fear of impotence which would mean psychiatric

$$\longrightarrow P \longleftarrow G \pm$$
$$M_1 \qquad M_2$$

Diagram 3

treatment, but more usually in practice he resolves the conflict by jilting the girl friend. At a much more elementary level the same basic conflict can be seen in the child who desires to pat a dog and yet is afraid of it.

The last type of conflict situation is when the person stands between two equally unattractive goals. He is repelled by both goals but the further he moves away from one, the nearer he moves to the other. A student may be faced with the situation of having to work hard at a subject he dislikes or risk failure in his examinations. The further he moves from the work situation, that is, the less work he does, the nearer he gets actually to failing his exam, an equally undesirable result from his point of view (Diagram 4). A child may be faced with the situation

$$G_1 - \longrightarrow P \longleftarrow G_2 -$$
$$M_1 \qquad M_2$$

Diagram 4

of having to go to bed early and so miss a favourite TV programme or staying up and incurring the disapproval of his father.

Reactions to Stress

By means of certain *mental dynamisms*, many of which were originally described by Freud, the mind can lessen the effects of frustration and thus diminish the degree of tension felt. If these mental dynamisms are used for solving all emotional difficulties they can and do lead to other symptoms as the person is no longer well adapted to the real world. However, mental dynamisms used sparingly are necessary for everyday life, as they protect the individual from minor degrees of anxiety and thus allow him to find not too unsatisfactory solutions to his problems.

Repression

Earlier in this chapter we saw that repression was the process whereby a patient rejects from consciousness those impulses and thoughts which are incompatible with his conscious motives or ideas of himself. The thoughts are "lost" because they are too painful to remember. A well-brought-up young man may be unable to accept the fact that he dislikes his father, so he represses all hate and all that is left is a slight feeling of uncomfortable tension when in his father's presence. A very similar mental dynamism is called *dissociation* and is seen in its most dramatic form in hysterical loss of memory. In these cases severe psychological stresses may occur at home or at work and the resulting anxiety builds up until it becomes unbearable. The person may then enter a peculiar fugue state during which he leaves the stressful environment by travelling many miles on a train or bus. Eventually he may be picked up by the police and brought to hospital where he is found to be suffering from total loss of memory. He not only fails to recall the psychological stresses in his environment but may also have forgotten anything that may help other people to bring him back to reality. He is, of course, at this stage completely free from anxiety and will usually remain so as long as he suffers from loss of memory. An interesting illustration of this was seen by one of the authors. This was a young man who was involved in smuggling cigarettes from Eire into Liverpool. After landing at Liverpool he went straight to the receivers, but there a severe quarrel took place. He was attacked and all his goods and money stolen. He wandered about the streets for the next two days and was brought into hospital suffering from loss of memory. The shock of losing all his worldly goods in a quarrel with those whom he had previosuly trusted proved too much for him. He had no solution for his problems except to forget them, which he did very effectively.

Projection

In this dynamism the person disguises his own unacceptable motives by ascribing them to other people. A man who is disgusted by minor expressions of sexual behaviour in himself may be constantly seeing sexual implications in other people's behaviour. Indeed some of these people appear to carry on campaigns in the press and describe all modern entertainments as disguised pornography. They are frequently men and women who are unable to accept the powerful sexual drives in themselves and, by projecting them on to other people, get some relief from their anxiety.

This dynamism is frequently seen in mental illness. A married woman was seen who was depressed and irritable. She was generally dissatisfied with life and appeared to have developed these symptoms because of attitudes she learned from her mother in adolescence. During the interview that followed she criticised her husband vehemently: he was the cause of all her troubles, he was unco-operative and would not give and take in their marriage. When actually seen the husband proved to be a pleasant, quiet, co-operative man who was at a loss to know how to help his wife. She had projected her own irritability and unco-operativeness on to her husband.

Displacement

In displacement the original object or goal of the motive is disguised by substituting another goal in its place. The substitute goal is usually more acceptable from the personal or social point of view. The classical example is seen in the old army story of the officer who tells off the sergeant, the sergeant tells off the corporal, the corporal tells off the private and the private kicks the dog. The workman who is told off by his boss goes home and plays hell with his wife. In young children this dynamism is frequently seen on the arrival of a baby brother or sister. If the child is very jealous and would like to hit the new arrival, it is usually deterred from this course of action and so destroys the new baby's Teddy bear instead. Outbreaks of violence on psychiatric wards are sometimes of this nature. A patient recently broke the windows of the interviewing room when there is no doubt he would really have liked to attack the doctor. Sometimes the displacement from one goal to another can be personally and socially very satisfactory. A married woman who has no children may take up nursing or looking after other people's children and find considerable happiness.

Rationalisation

In rationalisation the real explanation of the motives and the behaviour that follows is concealed, and a pseudo-rational explanation is given. This is seen in the student who fails his examination. Frequently he does not put this down to the true reason which is his lack of knowledge, but says that the examiner is prejudiced against him. The person who advocates corporal punishment as a solution to all behaviour problems in young people may be rationalising his own aggressive drives.

Sublimation

Freud believed that a frustrated drive such as the sexual drive could be diverted to provide energy for other creative activities such as art, music and literature. Freud, with his usual remarkable insight, felt that Leonardo da Vinci's interest in painting beautiful and serene Madonnas was really a sublimated expression of his longing for his own mother from whom he had separated at an early age. It is doubtful whether in most people biological drives such as the sexual drive can be diverted into other channels to any great degree. A study of the lives of the great painters and musicians lends little support to the idea that they lead celibate lives so as to provide energy and drive for their creative work. Sublimation may be regarded as a form of displacement.

Reaction Formation

In reaction formation the motive is expressed in a form that is directly opposite to its original intent. A person who is afraid of and dislikes another person may lean over backwards to be friendly to him. Some men, due to their upbringing, are afraid of softness in themselves and because of this try and indulge in everything and anything that is conventionally recognised as masculine behaviour. In parents of unwanted children one sometimes sees excessive displays of love and affection because they are afraid of their real feelings. In this case love is the crust on the pie that covers the meat of hate. Shakespeare was well aware of this when he made Hamlet's mother say of the Player Queen: " The lady protests too much, methinks."

Regression

In regression a person undergoing a motivational conflict or any other sort of psychological stress may retreat to a form of behaviour more appropriate at an earlier age. An adult may produce a behavioural pattern more like that of a child and a child may regress to acting like an infant. This type of behaviour is frequently seen in children. A child of 5 or 6 during its first day at school may wet itself after having been dry for perhaps a year or more. A child of 2 may temporarily lose the power of speech after the birth of a sister or brother. A boy of 14 or 15 if working under considerable pressure at home and at school may produce explosive outbursts of temper more appropriate to a nine-year-old. He may direct the temper into destructive channels by tearing up his books and thus displace the energy as well. Ill patients in hospital may become very dependent and child-like in their attitudes, and this may be due to a combination of psychological and physical stresses.

Identification

On a very general level identification is a group or social dynamism, A young doctor or medical student tends to identify himself with the medical profession as a whole. This topic is discussed more fully in Chapter 20, in terms of " role-playing ". At a more personal level the process of identification plays an important part in our development. The young boy may identify with his father or even an uncle and by that means learn to behave in a masculine way. Similarly, a young girl may identify with her mother. In adolescence, a schoolboy who is keen on sport may identify himself with some prominent athlete and try to copy his behaviour. In this way his own wishes receive some vicarious satisfaction.

Compensation

A handicapped person who is well aware of his handicap may compensate by overcoming it and becoming more than usually proficient in that very skill. A man who has a slight stutter may strive to overcome this by means of practice and public speaking and may end up as a great debater or orator. Many of our greatest speakers, especially in politics, appear to have had speech impediments as children. If it is impossible to master the handicap, a person may excel in other directions and so compensate for his handicap. Thus a cripple may make it his business to excel at intellectual activities because he cannot be an athlete.

Fantasy

An imaginary solution to a frustrated drive or motive can be temporarily satisfying. A person, by day-dreaming, may imagine all sorts of solutions to his desires and wishes, both possible and impossible. Sometimes this sort of day-dreaming leads to constructive solutions of his problems (see Chapter 3). The late teens and early twenties seem to be a period in life when day-dreaming is used as a frequent method of satisfying frustrated motives. The young man may dream of success with the opposite sex or of passing examinations without working. He may day-dream about being a successful surgeon in a dramatic moment in an operating theatre. As long as the person concerned can bring himself back to reality to tackle the real problems of his life no harm is done and indeed some good may result.

It is important to remember that the mind itself does not conveniently divide its reactions into clearly definable dynamisms. These dynamisms overlap and in any given circumstance several may be at work. Projection, rationalisation and identification may each be a suitable description either singularly or collectively of what is actually happening in a given case. The mind does not always react to stress by means of mental dynamisms. It learns to adapt its response so as to obtain the most desirable behaviour in any given set of circumstances.

Drug Taking

Unlike animals, men have always been able to employ artificial means of overcoming the effects of stress. These artificial means have been used with varying success throughout recorded history.

Indian hemp or *marihuana* is still widely used as an " escape mechanism " from the cares and troubles of the world. Smoking or ingestion seem to give a feeling of euphoria. Unfortunately, this effect is only short lived and the smoker has to come back to reality with none of his problems solved. Opium has been used in the Far East for the same reasons. This again introduces its own problems as opium (active constituent: morphine) produces a massive and terrifying addiction which prevents the individual from coping with his everyday life.

In western society opium alkaloids and preparations of the hemp weed have not yet gained the popularity of *tobacco* or *alcohol* (ethyl alcohol). Alcohol can act as a social lubricant at meetings, dances and parties, especially for the shy inhibited personality. This is also its danger, since such people may easily become dependent on it.

Perhaps the most interesting of all substances used in this way is *mescaline*. This substance has been used by certain Amero-Indian tribes. Mescaline produces dream like states in which the person sees visions of the " future " and relives his past. This property, in a similar substance known as *lysergic acid diethylamide* (L.S.D.), has been used by some psychiatrists to abreact their patients.

SELECTED BIBLIOGRAPHY

1. Two short accounts of psychoanalysis, Freud, S. (translated by James Strachey). 1962. London: Penguin.
   An excellent account of his earlier and later findings and ideas by the founder of psychoanalysis.
2. *A Dynamic Theory of Personality.* Lewin, K. 1935. New York: McGraw-Hill.
   Lewin's interesting field diagrams of conflict are fully explained.
3. *Frustration and Conflict.* Yates, A. J. 1962. London: Methuen.
   A complex and interesting account of experimentally produced conflict with an attempt to explain the facts by learning.
4. *Introduction to Psychology.* Morgan, C. T. 1956. New York: McGraw-Hill.
   See Chapter 10.

Chapter 9

PERSONALITY TRAITS, TYPES AND DIMENSIONS

Personality Traits

If we wished to describe someone so that they could be recognised later by a third person, or if we wished to record the important aspects of a patient's appearance and behaviour we should choose those aspects which were characteristic of him: that is the sort of clothes, or the sort of behaviour that he usually affected. These would be those things which he did repeatedly, and which we had come to associate with him. We should not describe him in terms of unusual or uncharacteristic behaviour which he only affected occasionally and which was out of keeping with his more usual self.

But merely noting the usual features of appearance and behaviour is not enough. It is quite possible to describe a person in terms of his appearance and behaviour quite accurately, and yet to say nothing worthwhile about him. Consider the following description:

> " Mr. X has a head, two eyes, a nose, a chin, and two ears. He frequently walks about, and swings his arms as he does so. He breathes, eats and sleeps at night. He wears more clothes in the winter than he does in the summer, and shivers when he is cold and sweats when he is hot. He feels cross at times and happy at others."

All we learn from a description of this sort is that Mr. X is a man like other men. This is, of course, because those features have been selected for the description which Mr. X shares with other people. They are not characteristic of him in the sense that they serve to distinguish him from others.

Now consider this description:

> " Mr. X is a short stout man, with a large red beard, rather protruding eyes and thick lips. He talks in a loud confident voice and tends to monopolise the conversation. He walks about with a heavy tread, and expects people to move out of his way. He is argumentative, quarrelsome and fiercely jealous of his reputation. He expects other people to defer to his opinions and believes his company is enjoyed and sought after."

We now have some idea of the kind of man Mr. X is, and may even have some sort of a mental picture of him. Thus there seem to be two important aspects of the statements made about people, if they are to be helpful in describing them. These are that such statements should be about enduring or oft-repeated features of the person's appearance and behaviour, and that they should be capable of differentiating that person from others. Statements of this sort that can usefully be made about other people refer to what are known as *personality traits*. A personality trait can be defined as: *An enduring or often repeated feature of a person's appearance or behaviour, by means of which he may be distinguished from others.*

Examples of traits of appearance are: " red-haired ", " blue-eyed ", " loose-limbed ", " fat ", " tidy ", " formal ". Traits of behaviour could be " friendly ", " absent-minded ", " punctual ", " active ", " sociable ". Allport, who has done a vast amount of work in this field, once made a list of all such trait names in the English language, and collected no fewer than 17,953. He noted that some traits depended on appearance, and others on behaviour, but he also showed that some were heavily dependent on the judgment of others. He gives such examples as " absurd ", " adorable ", " amusing " and " astonishing ", all of which depend on subjective judgments of the observer. Others might not agree with these descriptions of the person in question.

The Person and Personality

From this we can see that, whereas some traits depend on enduring and fairly unchanging physique and habitual patterns of behaviour, others are only displayed in certain situations or are heavily dependent on the judgment and personal attitudes of the observer. This fact has led to two rather different kinds of definition of personality: The biophysical or " substance " definitions, and the biosocial or " mask " definitions. The former kind refer to the man-as-he-really-is. This assumes that a personality is something which can be assessed by careful study, measurement or testing. It assumes that when we dig below the surface, behind all the shams, pretences and play-acting, we come to a relatively enduring and stable *person* who can be classified, assessed and measured. The nature of this person can be delineated by studying the enduring, predictable and often repeated personality traits. The latter type of definition, the biosocial, refers to the man-as-others-see-him. This is the popular use of the term " personality": that " zip " or sparkle that makes a person stand out from the ruck.

When the ancient Greeks acted in plays, the actor would hold a mask in front of his face and talk through it. If he were portraying a villain he would hold up a villainous mask, if he were acting the hero, he would use an heroic mask. Now the latin word for this mask was " persona ", a word which has given rise to our term " personality ". In this sense the personality is thought of as a mask we hold up to the public view, hiding our real selves behind it. Furthermore, this concept suggests that we have several masks of this kind, each of which we use in appropriate circumstances. This is in line with some modern ideas of role-playing, which are referred to in Chapter 20. We certainly behave differently in different situations, choosing the mask appropriate for the occasion. Nevertheless, there is a stamp, a style, which makes us recognisably ourselves, and the more we know a person the more we can recognise that the constantly changing patterns of appearance and behaviour do relate to the person as a whole. The various masks are adopted for consistent reasons with a series of goals in view which fit the personality considered " in depth ". Thus we can observe that a person gets angry in this or that situation and we can go further and ask: " Why do these sorts of situation anger him so much? " We might then discover that he becomes angry in situations where he was made to feel inferior, ignorant or lacking " savoir faire ". We could then speak of an " inferiority complex " and trace its development to childhood experiences. We should now be including in our concept of personality not only observable traits, but the dynamic interaction of all aspects of the person: his appearance, behaviour, thinking, emotions, attitudes, opinions, prejudices, passions and so on. Person-ality as we understand it then, must include inward and unseen events inferred from outward behaviour as well as the outward behaviour itself.

Before we give a working definition of personality, it is necessary to define some terms used in such a definition.

Physical traits refer to bodily shape, neuro-endocrine endowment, habits of posture, facial expression and so on.

Intellectual traits refer to intelligence, acquired knowledge, opinions, attitudes and interests. These are the cognitive traits.

Temperamental traits include habitual emotional responses to situations, and refer to whether a person is excitable or calm, easy-going or irritable, friendly or hostile. These are the affective traits.

Character traits refer to strength of will, tenacity of purpose and persistence in the face of difficulties. These are the conative traits.

Of course many, if not all, patterns of behaviour are complex interactions of two or more of these classes of trait. Attitudes and opinions are emotionally toned and affect our strength of will. Even our bodily build seems to be associated with the pattern of our emotional responses (see Chapter 11).

We can now define personality as: *The dynamic interaction of a person's physical, intellectual, temperamental and character traits as revealed in his appearance and behaviour, by which he may be distinguished as a unique individual.*

Trait Clusters and Personality Types

Not only do people display an enormous number of different personality traits, but such traits tend to appear in *clusters*. Thus certain physical traits may be frequently associated with certain temperamental traits, or some intellectual trait may be associated with some character trait, or again certain traits of each of the four kinds may appear frequently together. A pair of traditionally associated traits is red hair and bad temper. Another is small stature and self-assertiveness. A perusal of any Victorian melodrama will reveal that all innocent girls have large eyes set wide apart, and that they are likely to have fair hair and blue eyes. Shifty and mean characters have small eyes set close together, and strong-minded men have large prominent chins. The villain is almost certain to be dark haired and probably swarthy into the bargain. His lips will be thin if he is cruel, and thick and fleshy if he is sensual. Whether this sort of folk traditional correspondence between physiognomy and personality has any real basis is rather doubtful, but what is worth noting here is that it has long been considered that traits of all sorts do occur in clusters so that one can discern *personality types* which consist of recognisable clusters of traits which are frequently associated in the same people. Bain made an early attempt to do this. His book published in 1862 suggested that there were three types of person, according to whether their energies were concentrated on cognitive, affective or conative types of behaviour (Fig. 17). People who were mainly interested in cognitive experiences were the mental types, those who expressed themselves emotionally were the vital types, and those who were strong-minded dominating people were the volitional types.

The mental type was the tall, thin, weedy, shy, scholarly and dreamy person. He would be called " introverted " nowadays. The second was the short, fat, breezy, hearty, loud-mouthed, confident and sociable type. We should call him an " extravert " to-day. The third was the strong, silent, muscular, pipe-smoking leader of men. This sort of division seems to have some real basis as we shall see in Chapter 11. Bain's types will be recognised in the ectomorph, mesomorph and endomorph described in that chapter (see p. 107).

We have already referred to the well-known division into introvert and extravert types. These terms were introduced by Jung who suggested that the introvert was more concerned with the inner subjective world of fantasy than the extravert who was more interested in the outer world of practical reality. The introvert is governed by absolute principle, whereas the extravert is a " realist " and bows to necessity. The introvert tends to be rather rigid and inflexible in his reaction to life, whereas the extravert is adaptable and adjusts easily to changing situations. The introvert's delicacy of feeling is not shared by the extravert whose emotional reactions are rather crude and

Bain's Three Types

THE MENTAL TYPE

THE VOLITIONAL TYPE

THE VITAL TYPE

Fig. 17

undifferentiated. His emphasis on absolute standards make the introvert self-critical, a trait not shared by the extravert. Under stress the introvert tends to escape into his fantasy world, and if he breaks down tends to become anxious or obsessional. The extravert reacts to stress by some action leading, if possible, to some tangible compensation. If he breaks down his neurosis tends to be of the hysterical kind.

The trouble with any attempt to sort people out into clear-cut types, is that no-one really fits any particular type, and remains obstinately himself. There are very few people indeed who can be said to be " typical " and when we meet such a person they seem to be a caricature of the type they resemble.

Personality Dimensions

It is more fashionable nowadays to speak of *personality dimensions* rather than of types. It is easier to place people at various places along one or more dimensions of personality than to try and see them as conforming to some particular type. Possible dimensions might be height, intelligence, or excitability. This seems to work rather better

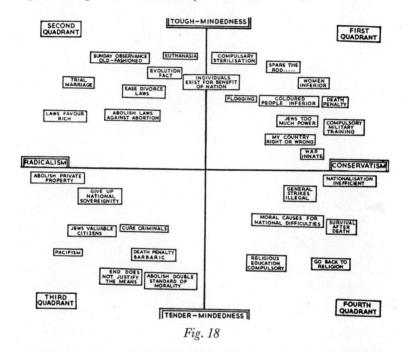

Fig. 18

than trying to fit people into ready-made types, and in the end to be more convincing. The task now is not so much to discern types to which people approximate, but rather to discover the most relevant and meaningful dimensions along which people can be placed. Moreover by combining two dimensions we can see how people in various parts of the area defined by them, tend to exhibit various clusters of traits. Just the same could be done by choosing two physiological dimensions such as blood pressure and B.M.R., and seeing how people in various parts of the area defined by these two dimensions exhibited various signs and symptoms.

As an example of this sort of enquiry, we shall quote some work of Eysenck. He plotted people on two dimensions: tough-minded-tender-minded, and radical-conservative. This sort of thing can be done mathematically from material gained from questionnaires, the answers to which are analysed statistically (Fig. 18). It will be seen how opinions and attitudes cluster. People who think women are inferior

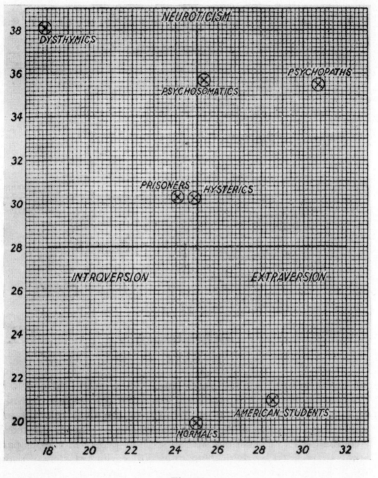

Fig. 19

also tend to believe in corporal punishment, the death-penalty, racial discrimination, compulsory military training and so on. These are the tough-minded conservatives. On the other hand, those who believe in survival after death would also like religious education to be compulsory, blame moral causes for national difficulties and think strikes should be made illegal. These are the tender-minded conservatives.

Eysenck himself has chosen two dimensions which he thinks can be usefully employed in assessing personality in the clinical field. One is the introversion-extraversion dimension already described, and the other is a dimension stable-neurotic. Various clinical groups seem to cluster in various parts of the area defined by these dimensions (Fig. 19). *Dysthymics* (which include anxiety, obsessions, and depression as symptoms) seem to be neurotic introverts. *Hysterics* seem to be more extraverted than dysthymics, and also more neurotic than the normal group. This supports Jung's theory of the breakdown patterns of introverts and extraverts mentioned earlier. *Psychopaths* (which include a group of egocentric people who are said to have little or no social conscience, and to be incapable of making good relationships with other people) seem to be neurotic extraverts.

Assessing Personality

Eysenck claims that there are a number of *objective behaviour tests* which can provide information which enables an individual to be placed along a dimension. The trait of persistence has been shown to be associated with the dimension of introversion, so that a test of persistence might help us to say how introverted a person was. One simple test of persistence is to get a person to sit on a chair and to ask him to hold one leg out in front of him with the heel about an inch above the seat of a second chair. He is then timed to see how long he can hold his leg up in that position. There are wide individual differences in the length of time people can do this, which seems to depend on their persistence rather than on the strength of their muscles or the weight of their legs. Some people put up with discomfort better than others, and seem more determined to continue with a task in the face of such discomfort. Another objective behaviour test assesses a trait that is thought to be associated with the dimension of neuroticism. This is the trait of suggestibility. The test consists of making a person believe he is swaying forward so much that swaying actually occurs. A person is stood with his back to a wall, with a thread from his collar which passes over a pulley fixed to the wall. This is attached to a weight which hangs down against a vertical scale. The subject is blindfolded and then told repeatedly that he is swaying forward. This is usually done by playing the repeated suggestion on a tape-recorder. The amount of sway that actually occurs is measured by the distance up the scale the weight is moved as the person sways forwards. Again there are wide individual differences in the amount of sway produced, and in this way the degree of suggestibility is measured. The first test, then, can be used as a measure of extraversion and the second as a measure of neuroticism.

A more convenient way of measuring these two dimensions is by using a *questionnaire* containing questions that have been found to be valid measures of either extraversion or neuroticism. Such a questionnaire is the Maudsley Personality Inventory. Typical questions would be as follows:

A person might be considered extraverted, or rather would add to his extraversion score, if he answered " Yes " to:

1. Do you like to mix socially with people?
2. Are you happiest when you get involved in some project that calls for rapid action.

Or if he answered " No " to:

1. Are you inclined to keep to the background on social occasions?
2. Are you inclined to limit your acquaintances to a select few?

A person might be considered neurotic, or rather would add to his neuroticism score, if he answered " Yes " to:

1. Do you ever feel " just miserable " for no good reason at all?
2. Do ideas run through your head so that you cannot sleep?
3. Do you have periods of such great restlessness that you cannot sit long in a chair?

People could also be assessed on a *rating-scale* by independent observers. For example a person could be assigned to one of five positions along a rating scale for irritability.

1. Never gets irritable.
2. Very occasionally irritable.
3. Irritable in appropriate circumstances.
4. Irritable most of the time.
5. Always irritable.

An average person would be rated at point 3, good-tempered people at 1 or 2, and bad-tempered people at 4 or 5.

Both these methods have their limitations. The purport of questionnaires is often too painfully obvious to the person being questioned, who will sometimes try and present himself in a favourable light, and conceal some traits which he considers to be undesirable. On the other hand a person might judge himself rather harshly, and present himself much more unfavourably than others would. For this reason the rating scale method is used, especially when it is possible to obtain independent ratings of subjects by a number of different observers. Even here, as some workers have found, it is difficult to avoid what is known as the " halo effect ". This happens when one subject quickly impresses an observer who is then, perhaps quite unconsciously, inclined to notice all the good points and ignore all the bad. The possibilities of this sort of thing happening were discussed in Chapter 2. Equally an observer could become prejudiced against a subject so that he noticed the bad points and ignored the good.

We have already mentioned the problem of considering personality in depth, and the complications arising from motivation of which the subject is unaware. This clearly would affect the answers to a questionnaire, which could only be based on the ideas of which the subject were aware.

As many workers have pointed out, one can only begin to know a person well after prolonged and repeated observation of him in different moods and different circumstances. We might meet a person for the first time and judge him to be aggressive in speech and manner, always trying to score off people or to prove them wrong. As we get to know him we might begin to realise that this outward aggression was covering a more fundamental timidity and insecurity. A person who might appear at first to be pleasantly modest and unassuming, might later reveal that this modesty was in fact a cloak for a colossal conceit.

These difficulties in assessing a personality in depth, as it were, can to some extent be got over by the use of what are known as *projective techniques*. In Chapter 2 we saw that perception is largely a matter of interpreting stimuli and making meaning of them. This can only be done on the basis of past experience. The less clear and distinct the stimuli, or the more ambiguous their nature, the more does the perceiver have to provide interpretations from his own store of past experiences. Therefore projective tests consist of ambiguous or vague stimuli which the subject is asked to interpret in some way.

The most famous of these is the Rorschach Test which consists of inkblots, some in black ink, others made up of various blots made from coloured inks. These blots, of which there is a standard series of ten, are then presented one at a time to the subject who is asked to say what he thinks the blots look like, and what he can see in them. Responses range from concrete specific answers such as a " bat flying " or " a bird sitting on the branch of a tree ", to such abstract responses as " this gives me a feeling of power " or " this symbolises evil ". With experience of the range of responses obtainable from a wide variety of different personalities, some psychologists can gain valuable insights into the person they are studying. Other tests of this nature consist of clear-cut pictures, to which the subject has to make up a story. These pictures clearly represent themes of parent-child relationships, sibling rivalry, sexual themes, depression and violence. In order to make up stories to fit such pictures the subject has to draw on his own past experience, and may reveal attitudes and prejudices about the situations he is describing.

The advantages of these techniques are that they probe below the surface, and the subject does not always know or realise how much he is revealing about himself. The import of his responses is much less clear in this type of test than it is in answers to straight questionnaires. For this reason it is usually held to be unethical to invite a person to do a personality test of this sort without warning him that it is hoped to gain some insight into aspects of his personality which may be kept hidden in normal circumstances. People usually accept this situation, especially if they have come to the doctor for help. It seems that although they object to answering intimate and personal questions about themselves, people are willing to do personality tests despite the fact that they are perfectly aware that in doing so they might reveal hidden aspects of their personality.

SELECTED BIBLIOGRAPHY

1. *Pattern and Growth in Personality.* Allport, G. W. 1963. London: Holt.
2. *Introduction to Psychology.* Morgan, C. T. 1956. New York: McGraw-Hill. Chapter 9.

Chapter 10

PHYSICAL ASPECTS OF EMOTIONS

Since the earliest times in literature, philosophy and clinical medicine, emotions have been associated with the production of physical symptoms and diseases. Indeed so close has been this association between the mental and physical aspect of emotions that in our language emotions are frequently described in physical terms. A person who is frightened is described as being in a " cold sweat " or turning " pale ". A person who is sad or dejected is said to be " down at the mouth " or " fed up ". The very fact that the most prominent physical aspects of emotion were manifest in the viscera led to the erroneous belief that the seat of the emotions was actually in the chest or abdomen.

Components of Emotions

Emotions are complex responses produced by the animal or human being as it reacts with its environment. Some emotional responses are inborn while others are acquired by learning, but in the adult human being most are a combination of the two. Many emotional reactions occur when some inner drive is prevented from reaching its goal (see Chapter 7).

The *emotional experience* is perhaps the only component of an emotion which, when present, means that the emotion is actually taking place. If a person feels sad or happy he can be said to be undergoing that emotional change even if the other components are not detectable. It is possible for the experience of an emotion not to be fully conscious and for the person concerned not to recognise its true nature. The psycho-analytical movement started by Freud was concerned mainly with this type of emotional experience and its effect on the personality. Even in these " unconscious " or disguised emotions it is quite often possible to observe the other emotional components.

Certain patterns of *emotional expression* and *behaviour* are a consistent accompaniment of particular emotions, especially in mammals. When a cat is " angry " it arches its back, raises its tail, bares its teeth and gives a peculiar hissing noise. We know it is angry because we have observed its behaviour in many situations that should make a cat angry and it usually produces this characteristic response. However, it is not " angry " in the human sense of the word and we have no means of knowing just what a cat feels under these circumstances. Indeed with our very different brain it is unlikely that we ever experience anything like " cat anger ". All we can say is that from a phylogenetic point of view the more the brain of an animal differs from our own the greater is the difficulty in distinguishing its emotional reactions. It would need very careful observation to know whether a fish was angry, sad or happy. The most we could say would be that it was " fish happy " or " fish sad ".

In human beings it is not always easy to detect the emotions felt from a study of the behaviour of the person concerned. The one emotional pattern that is common to all human beings and indeed some of the higher primates is the *startle response*. This is produced by creeping up to a person and shouting in his ear or by banging a door in a room that was previously quiet. The eyes close rapidly, the head thrusts forward with the chin raised, the mouth widens (like a grin) and the neck muscles become prominent. Emotional patterns other than the startle response vary from person to person and especially from culture to culture, which suggests that these patterns are mainly learnt. It is possible however to classify all emotions into two main groups and to discern in these groups contrasting physical reactions. The two groups are:

1. Emotions such as joy, happiness, contentment (referred to in Chapter 7 as *reward emotions*).
2. Emotions such as fear, disgust, anger (referred to in Chapter 7 as *drive emotions*).

In the reward emotions the mouth widens, turns up and the eyes tend to shut. In the drive emotions the mouth shrinks, turns down and the eyes also tend to shut.

Physiological Changes in the Body Excluding the C.N.S.

Most emotions are accompanied by some change in the autonomic nervous system. No known emotion is purely a sympathetic or a parasympathetic reaction but a complex dynamic balance between the two. The work of Cannon emphasised the part played by the sympathetic nervous system in some emotional states, especially fear and anxiety. The heart rate increases, blood pressure rises due to peripheral vasoconstriction, the pupils dilate, hairs become erect and liver glycogen is mobilised producing a rise in the blood glucose level. Secretion of adrenaline by the adrenal medulla reinforces this sympathetic activity. This is the classical picture of the sympathetic system preparing the animal for fight or flight in the face of danger. However, the situation is not as clear cut as that, as anyone knows who has waited for an oral examination. Frequency of micturition, which is mainly a parasympathetic activity, is common during anxiety.

It is difficult to distinguish between similar emotions on a purely autonomic basis, but if one takes two contrasting emotions such as *anger*, and *affection* of a mother for her child, certain differences become apparent.

Anger (drive emotion)	Affection (reward emotion)
Tense bodily movements	Relaxed movements
Harsh voice	Soft voice
Vasoconstriction or dilation of arterioles	Vasodilation
Pupils dilated	Pupils dilated
Contraction of gastro-intestinal tract	Relaxation of gastro-intestinal tract
Dry mouth	Moist mouth
Sweating	Slight sweating

Even in these two emotions the differences are not as large as might be imagined.

Emotions and the Stomach

In the late 1940s Wolf and Wolff made a series of observations on the effect of emotional states on the stomach of an individual called " Tom ". Tom had a permanent opening to his stomach situated in his abdominal wall due to a previous surgical gastrostomy. This chronic gastric fistula allowed direct observation to the mucous membrane of the subject to be made under all sorts of psychological situations. Observations made included: 1. Colour and secretion of the gastric mucosa. 2. Changes in temperature of the gastric mucosa by means of a thermocouple. 3. Quantity and quality of the gastric secretion especially the hydrochloric acid. 4. Gastric mobility.

Whenever Tom became angry or showed aggression his gastric mucosae would become red, engorged and congested. Small spots of blood would appear both on and beneath the surface, especially on touching with a glass rod, and occasionally the mucous membrane would break down and a small superficial ulcer appear. The quantity of hydrochloric acid secreted increased and muscular contractions of the stomach became frequent.

During states of depression and dejection Tom's stomach become pale, the gastric secretion decreased and normal mobility was inhibited.

If at this stage he was fed with beef broth the normal increase in blood supply, secretions and mobility did not take place.

If Tom was given a sudden fright the mucous membrane would become pale and the secretions tended to dry up.

Later work by others has shown that not all individuals produce the same gastric reactions as Tom. There are individual variations, but many produce a pattern of response similar to that obtained by Wolf and Wolff. Engels and his colleagues observed the gastric secretions of 59 infants between the ages of 15 to 20 months who had had an artificial gastric fistula produced so as to relieve an oesophageal atresia. Anger and aggression was again associated with high hydrochloric acid output and mucosal redness while depression produced low hydrochloric acid output, and paleness of the mucosa.

Emotions and the Cardiovascular System

The whole pattern of cardiovascular output can be altered during emotional states. Hickam and his co-workers as early as 1948 demonstrated this in medical students. They took 23 medical students and measured their cardiovascular output and metabolic rate two days before an important examination and two days after the same examination. The cardiovascular output before the examination was two litres/minute greater than after, and the metabolic rate was double the post-examination rate.

Emotions and Renal Function

The functions of the kidney and the salt and water metabolism of the body in general are bound up with the emotional state of the individual. In a masterly series of demonstrations Schottstaedt, Grace and Wolff in 1956 threw much light on the subject. They studied five patterns of emotional responses in human subjects and at the same time measured various aspects of renal function. During periods of mild tension and alert behaviour (pattern a) a decrease in water and salt excretion occurred associated with an increase in creatinine excretion. As soon as the subjects were allowed to relax (pattern b) a mild diuresis occurred which was not accompanied by any increased output of sodium and potassium ions. During periods of excitement and apprehension (pattern c) a diuresis occurred which was associated with an increased excretion of sodium and potassium ions and creatinine. The same sort of physiological changes occurred when the subjects became aggressive or felt angry (pattern d). In situations characterised by futility and feelings of depression (pattern e) water and sodium and potassium ions were retained. These changes are summarised as follows:

Emotional reaction	a	b	c	d	e
Excretion rate of water	−	+	+	+	−
Excretion rate of sodium and potassium ions	−	o	+	+	−
Excretion rate of creatinine	+	o	+	+	−

Increased rate of excretion	+	Relaxation after pattern a	b
Decreased rate of excretion	−	Excitement and apprehension	c
No change in excretion rate	o	Aggression and anger	d
Mild tension and alert behaviour	a	Depression	e

Some Blood Changes in Emotional States

The relationship of the blood clotting mechanism to emotional stress is very important, as this mechanism plays an important part in the causation of several common diseases. The clotting mechanism appears to respond to emotional stress in two entirely different ways. According to Schneider and others, when the subject reacts to psychological stresses with anxiety, fear, hostility or anger, the clotting time and prothrombin time are shortened while the blood viscosity is increased.

Emotional state	Fear or anger	Dejection or depression
Clotting time	−	+
Prothrombin time	−	+
Blood viscosity	+	o

Decreased —   Increased +   No change o

It is well known that coronary thrombosis, in which a blood clot is formed in one of the main coronary arteries of the heart, is liable to be precipitated by severe anxiety or suppressed anger. During periods of depression the exact opposite occurs. The clotting time and the prothrombin time are both increased although the blood viscosity remains unchanged.

Emotions and the Endocrine Glands

Like all the other systems discussed so far the endocrine glands are profoundly affected by the emotional state of the individual. It is well known that in patients waiting to undergo surgical operations there is a marked increase in the secretion by the anterior pituitary gland of adrenocorticotrophic hormone and, as a result, of hydrocortisone by the adrenal cortex. Indeed it is thought by some people that this mechanism is one of the fundamental ways in which the body deals with both physical and psychological stress.

In a book of this size it is not possible to deal with the physiological effects of emotional changes in any great detail, but sufficient data have been given to show that these changes are real and play some part in the causation of diseases, especially the so-called "stress diseases". There are in fact marked individual variations between the physiological reaction of one subject as compared with another when subjected to similar psychological stresses. These differences are due to two main factors. The first is the personality structure of the individual concerned. How a person reacts emotionally to a given situation depends upon his constitution and life experience and hence upon the structure of his personality. The second factor is the particular physiological constitution of the individual; the reactivity and responsiveness of the autonomic nervous system and which particular organ or set of organs are most affected by psychological stress. For instance in certain diseases of the colon, marked changes in the blood supply of the mucous membrane are produced by psychological stress, whereas in normal subjects such changes are only just detectable (see Chapter 11).

Physiological Changes in the C.N.S.

Various physiological changes have been detected in the C.N.S. of animals, especially in mammals undergoing emotional reactions. It is useful to try and separate those changes that occur during both somatic and visceral emotional expression, from those that occur during emotional experiences or awareness. In the intact animal both occur together and are linked to each other.

The head ganglia of the autonomic nervous system which controls the functioning of the viscera and of some of the endocrine glands are also concerned in emotional expression and experience. The forebrain of mammals contains three main centres or systems which control the autonomic functions of the body. Briefly these centres are as follows:

1. Lowest centre in the diencephalon—hypothalamus.
2. Limbic system or the "visceral brain" of McLean.
3. Highest centre in the frontal lobe, especially the orbital surface.

It will be instructive to deal with each of these centres in turn and to try and indicate its relationship to emotional reactions.

Emotions and the Hypothalamus

The hypothalamus is situated in the diencephalon ventral to the thalamus, ventro-medial to the third ventricle and dorsal to the pituitary gland (see Chapter 6, Fig. 15, p. 61). In the late 1920s Bard began a series of experiments in which he demonstrated the part played by the hypothalamus and adjacent structures in the mediation of emotional expression. He used the cat as his experimental animal almost all the time and this proved to be very useful as it allowed him to compare some of his later experiments with his earlier ones.

In his earlier experiments the brain of the cat was divided rostral to the hypothalamus. When the animal had recovered from the effects of the operation its behaviour was carefully observed. A noxious stimulus such as a sharp pinprick produced a furious excitable reaction which Bard called *sham rage*. This consisted of the cat's arching its back, lashing its tail and biting or scratching anything that was in its reach. At the same time its pupils dilated, the blood pressure rose, the heart rate increased, hairs became erect and it started to sweat on the toe pads. This sham rage was " anger " completely out of control and was elicited by stimuli of such small intensity that they usually produced little or no effect on normal animals. The anger was not directed against anything or anybody.

In a later experiment he divided the brain between the mid-brain and the hypothalamus, and when this was done only a few scattered components of "sham rage" could be elicited by a noxious stimulus, of which the most prominent was tail lashing. Bard decided that the hypothalamus, especially the posterior part, was necessary for the co-ordinated expression of " sham rage ".

This work of Bard was confirmed by Masserman who introduced fine electrodes into the hypothalamic region of the cat's brain under anaesthesia. On recovery stimulation of the hypothalamus by the electrodes produced a typical rage reaction. Again the rage was not directed against anything.

Bard had pointed out that it was unlikely that the animal felt or was aware of any emotion during " sham rage ". He had noted that in between two bouts of rage the animal would consume food normally. Indeed Bard used the term " sham rage " which he borrowed from Cannon to indicate that the rage was not felt.

Emotions and the Limbic System

The smell brain or rhinencephalon was thought until recently to be exclusively concerned with the perception of odours. However, von

The Limbic Lobe

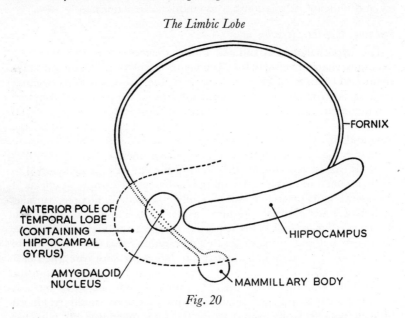

Fig. 20

Papez and later on McLean suggested that in the higher animals and in human beings it may have an even more important function concerned with emotional and autonomic integration. The exact extent of the limbic system which McLean called the "visceral brain" has never been fully agreed upon by workers in this field. Most people would include the amygdaloid nucleus, hippocampus, the fornix and perhaps the mammillary bodies. Some of the overlying cerebral cortex such as the hippocampal gyrus, dentate gyrus and the cingulate gyrus are also thought by others to be essential. (See Figure 20).

It was Bard and Mountcastle who first investigated this system in any detail. They found that on removal of the neocortex of a cat but leaving most of the limbic system intact the animal became remarkably placid. Painful stimuli would elicit no angry or aggressive reactions and sometimes the animal would start to purr or show affectionate behaviour. If, later on, large parts of the limbic system were removed the animal became capable of showing " angry reactions " which were much more refined than the crude " sham rage " discussed earlier.

Later on Kluver and Bucy in a series of experiments confirmed this general impression. They performed bilateral removal of the anterior parts of the temporal lobes of wild macaque monkeys. These monkeys became very placid and neither fear nor anger could be aroused in them. They tended to put all objects they could get hold of into their mouths and indulged in indiscriminate excessive sexual activity. Very similar results have since been obtained in animals by removal of only the amygdaloid nucleus. McLean has since shown by means of electrical and chemical stimulation of the hippocampus that marked grooming and pleasure reactions can be produced in cats. The exact meaning of all the experimental work performed on the limbic system is rather difficult to elucidate. As a tentative hypothesis it appears that as soon as various parts of the limbic system are released from higher control exaggerated emotional reactions of usually the pleasure-seeking kind take place. The animal appears to feel these emotions and even to direct its behaviour so as to elicit them.

Emotional Reactions and the Frontal Lobe

The frontal lobe is concerned with the highest level of control and integration of emotional reactions. It shares this function in some degree with the cingulate gyrus and other cortical parts of the limbic system.

A great deal is known about the effects of removal of the frontal lobe on human beings. This is because various neurosurgical procedures involving the frontal lobe have been used for many years in the treatment of certain intractable psychiatric conditions (see Chapter 14). Part of or all of the frontal lobe has been separated from the rest of the brain and the effects on the general physiology and behaviour of the patients observed.

Probably the most consistent change observed is a reduction of the intensity of all the congenital and acquired biological and social inhibitions. This leads the patient to become tactless and boastful in speech. He tends to make silly inappropriate jokes and is at times crude and excessive in his sexual demands. His general appetite increases and he loses the feeling of anxiety or fear even when one would expect such emotions. His general emotional tone is one of euphoria and he has little feeling for other people. Contrary to what was originally thought, few if any intellectual changes are apparent. It is difficult to sum up the part played by the central nervous system in the expression and awareness of emotions. The precise physiological changes which influence our emotional awareness are affected by the endocrine system as well as the C.N.S. The hypothalamus acts as a link between the endocrine system and the limbic system. The basic patterns of emotional expression appear to be carried out by the hypothalamus and these patterns are refined and controlled by the visceral brain at which level awareness also seems to take place. A more general inhibition of pleasurable emotional responses seems to be mediated through the cerebral cortex, especially the frontal lobe. At this stage it is important to note the part played by certain portions of the limbic system in retention of memories. There is a very marked psychological link between emotions and memories of particular events. When particular memories are brought to light under hypnosis they are usually accompanied by the emotions which were present at the time of the original events. This of course is much easier to understand from the physiological point of view when it is realised that the limbic system is concerned with both emotions and the reproduction of memories.

SELECTED BIBLIOGRAPHY

1. *Human Gastric Functions.* Wolf, S. and Wolff, H. G. 1943. London: Oxford University Press.
   A very interesting and stimulating account of " Tom " in all sorts of peculiar situations.
2. *The Limbic System (Visceral Brain) and Emotional Behaviour.* McLean, P. D. 1955. Arch. Neurol & Psychiat. 73. 130–134.
   A general account of McLean's ideas and concepts.
3. *Emotion and Emotional Disorders.* Gellhorn, E. and Loofbourrow, G. N. 1963. New York: Harper and Row.
   An exhaustive study of the subject packed full of facts and expressing some of the authors' highly original ideas.

Chapter 11

PHYSIQUE, TEMPERAMENT AND PSYCHOSOMATIC RELATIONSHIPS

Throughout history physicians and philosophers have attempted to relate physique and temperament to susceptibility to various kinds of disorder. Early attempts to classify physique and temperament left little room for the person who did not fit into such rigid categories.

In ancient Greece, Hippocrates divided his patients into two groups: *habitus phthisicus* and *habitus apoplecticus*. The first group consisted of thin weedy individuals, with round shoulders, apt to develop chest disorders; while the second group was composed of fat, muscular individuals with large abdomens who tended to suffer from strokes. Hippocrates was an acute observer and noticed that his habitus apoplecticus suffered from attacks of severe depression, which he attributed to an excess of " black bile " hence the term *melancholia*. He thus linked a particular physique not only with a proneness to develop certain types of physical ailments, but also to develop a particular type of mental illness. During the late middle ages it became accepted folk-lore that temperament and physique were linked. Shakespeare gives two typical examples of this in his plays. He links Falstaff's fat, muscular, short-necked physique with his jolly, pleasure-loving, sensual and energetic temperament. Julius Caesar describes Cassius as " lean and hungry " adding that " he thinks too much ".

Later on, in the nineteenth and early twentieth centuries, many physicians, psychologists and philosophers produced classifications, but it was not until the 1920s that any real progress was made. In a book called *Physique and Character*, published in 1925, the psychiatrist Kretschmer described three types of physique: 1. *Pyknic*—people with large visceral cavities, small shoulder girdles, fat on the trunk and thighs and small hands and feet. 2. *Asthenic*—tall people with narrow shoulders, flat chests, long limbs, poor musculature, loose skin and little fat. 3. *Athletic*—broad-shouldered people with very well-developed muscles. He was impressed by the apparent correlation between body build and the various types of mental illness. Patients who suffered from severe depressive illnesses tended to be of pyknic build and those suffering from schizophrenia were usually asthenic in type and occasionally athletic. Very severe epileptics such as those found in psychiatric hospitals tended also to be athletic. Kretschmer studied the relationship between the patient's pre-morbid personality, the mental illness and his physical build. He came to the conclusion that certain personalities were more likely to be found in people of particular body builds. The cyclothymic tended to have a pyknic physique. This is the person subject to mood swings, who sometimes feels on top of the world, and at other times depressed and irritable. The shy, retiring, serious personality who was fond of reading and studying tended to have an asthenic physique. The aggressive personality tended to be of athletic build. It was apparent from the beginning that Kretschmer's scheme was only a first approximation. In practice few people are typically pyknic, asthenic or athletic in build. The majority are somewhere in between these three types.

This problem was tackled by Sheldon about twenty years ago. By means of photographing hundreds of young men, he was able to abstract three distinct *components* of physique. He called his first component *endomorphy* and described it as a relative preponderance of soft roundness throughout the various regions of the body. When present as a marked feature, the digestive viscera tended to be massive as did most of the structures derived from the embryonic endoderm. The second component he called *mesomorphy* which was a preponderance of muscle, bone and connective tissue derived from mesodermal tissues. The body tended to be heavy, hard and rectangular in outline. The last component he called *ectomorphy* by which he meant a relatively marked linearity and fragility. The ectomorph had a very large surface area in relationship to his weight and also a large central nervous system. Each component was rated on a scale with a maximum of 7 and a minimum of 1. Every person has some of each of these components present. The profile that a subject presented he called the *somatotype*. The average person tended to have a physique made up as follows:

Endomorphy	Mesomorphy	Ectomorphy
4	4	4

While the very muscular or athletic person would have a somatotype such as:

Endomorphy	Mesomorphy	Ectomorphy
1	7	2

The pyknic physique on Sheldon's scale would be as follows:

Endomorphy	Mesomorphy	Ectomorphy
7	3	2

The next stage in Sheldon's work was to try and measure temperament. From numerous trait names describing such aspects of personality as aggressiveness, emotionality, and energy level, he selected under one hundred and used these traits on which to rate a large group of college students. From the results he managed to abstract three main temperamental types. These were:

1. *Viscerotonia*, characterised by love of comfort, eating and social activities associated with relaxation.
2. *Somatotonia*, characterised by a desire for muscular activity, aggressiveness, and an energetic love of power.
3. *Cerebrotonia*, characterised by shyness, restraint, love of privacy, hypersensitivity and love of intellectual pursuits.

Each temperament was again represented on a seven-point scale with a maximum of 7 and a minimum of 1. Sheldon found that there was a correlation of about 0.8 between his components of physique and his temperamental types. Endomorphy was correlated with viscerotonia, mesomorphy with somatotonia and ectomorphy with cerebrotonia. Sheldon and his colleagues found that delinquents as a group tended to be mesomorphic in physique and to have a predominence of somatotonia in their personalities (Fig. 21). Although Sheldon's work was a great step forward it does seem that in many ways it was an oversimplification of the problem. Parnell working with Oxford students obtained lower correlations.

Cerebrotonia   Viscerotonia   Somatotonia

Fig. 21

How is it possible to explain these findings? There may be a common biological basis to both physique and temperament. The central nervous system and the endocrine system are largely determined by inherited factors and obviously influence both physical build and temperament. However, another explanation is also possible. People tend to form an image of themselves and react to events and other people in a way that social custom and pressure demand.   Their physique plays an important part in this image.   The fat endomorph expects and is expected to be jolly and sociable while the muscular mesomorph sees himself as tough and aggressive.   The truth, as always, probably lies somewhere between the two explanations.

Psychosomatic Relationships

The study of psychosomatic relationships, that is the reciprocal influence of the mind on the body in the causation of disease is not new.   Competent physicians have always taken into account emotional and personality factors in the treatment of any individual.   For the purpose of this chapter we shall use Halliday's definition of a psychosomatic disorder as " *a bodily disorder whose nature can be appreciated only when emotional disturbances are investigated in addition to physical disturbances* ". In the main it is the production of physiological disturbances and structural changes in the body as a result of personality difficulties or emotional changes that are of most interest.   Of course, once these physical changes have taken place their very nature will also have an effect on the patient's personality and emotions.   It is not useful to include under the definition of psychosomatic disorders those physical diseases which produce psychological symptoms, as for example tumours of the adrenal medulla which are accompanied by moderately severe anxiety, or personality disorders resulting from brain damage. (see Chapter 19).

Many of the more complex disorders known to modern medicine are not caused by any one factor in a simple way, but rather by a number of different factors acting together on the individual.   It is in these conditions that the psychosomatic approach is so fruitful.   To take only one example, in coronary thrombosis, inherited, dietary, racial, personality and emotional factors all seem to play a part.   When considering the psychosomatic relationships in a particular individual it is very important to consider all aspects of that individual and his environment.   Firstly, the patient's personality must be assessed in some detail and its weakness and strength delineated.   Then a study must be made of the patient's immediate social, work, and family environment. By comparing the immediate environment and the personality it is possible to ascertain what contemporary stresses are acting on the individual and whether these are likely to produce emotional responses either physically or mentally.   Experiences in childhood can sensitise an individual to stresses in the present environment.   A child who for various reasons was frightened of an elder brother may produce the same sort of emotional response in the presence of elder males, even when grown up.   If this response is repressed for any reason it is more likely to produce marked physiological changes in the viscera. Different individuals produce varying physiological changes under emotional tension. In one person it may be the stomach that is most affected, in another the colon and in yet a third the bronchioles of the respiratory system. It is probably a combination of three factors: differing personalities, differing environments and different physiological make-up, that determines which individual will actually get a psychosomatic disorder, which will get a mental breakdown and which will show no apparent adverse reaction of any sort.

There are three ways in which psychosomatic disorders can arise: 1. By the physical disturbances having a direct symbolic meaning for the patient. 2. As a direct result of the physiological disturbance produced by an emotional upset acting on a sensitised organ system. 3. By conditioning a particular physiological disturbance so that it occurs under lesser degrees of the same stress or even symbolically related stresses. The first way has been discussed in Chapter 19. Probably the most common reaction of this type is that associated with disturbances of heart rate. Under some sort of prolonged mild stress the patient's heart rate goes up. He then starts to get all the associated physical symptoms of a fast heart rate such as palpitations, discomfort in the chest and throbbing in the head. He may have heard of a near acquaintance suffering from heart disease who has had similar symptoms. He then starts to fear that he may have heart disease and thus a vicious circle is set up. Even if the original stress disappears the symptoms may persist because of the association with the fear of heart disease. It is the symbolic meaning of the symptoms for the patient, which in this case is heart disease and the fear of death, that keeps them going.

That emotional disturbances can produce physiological upsets in themselves is a matter of common observation (see Chapter 10). Some anxious people undergoing psychological stress suffer from severe indigestion while in others diarrhoea is produced. The particular organ or system primarily affected seems to be dependent upon the innate constitution of the person and upon environmental factors which have sensitised the organ concerned. The third way in which a psychosomatic disorder may be produced is perhaps the most important and certainly the most interesting. To begin with a particular psychological stress acting on a certain personality produces an emotional response. The physiological aspects of this emotional response become linked directly to the psychological stress. By means of conditioning (see Chapter 4) the physiological response is gradually produced by milder and milder psychological stress. At the same time it may become linked with other environmental happenings which were not in the first place stressful. In this way a neutral environmental change is linked to a physiological disturbance. If the physiological disturbance is frequent and severe enough, a psychosomatic disturbance can take place in which structural changes can occur.

Groen and van der Valk of the Dutch school of psychosomatic medicine have illustrated clearly just how these psychosomatic disorders are produced. They had under their observation a young man who was suffering from ulcerative colitis. This is a condition in which the mucous membrane of the large intestine becomes inflamed and ulcerated and in which there is a marked tendency for the ulcerated patches to bleed. In an effort to control the condition he had had the descending colon brought to the surface of the abdomen so as to create an artificial opening. This gave Groen and van der Valk a unique opportunity of studying the condition of the mucous membrane. The patient was a reserved person who had great difficulty in expressing his emotions overtly. It was of little use asking him directly how he felt.

Changes in colour and size in the Colon of a patient undergoing a therapeutic interview

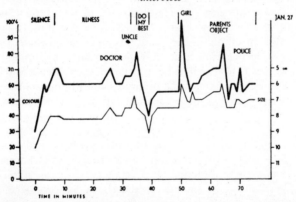

Induced silence increased hyperæmia and tone of the colonic segment; the condition remained unchanged when the illness was discussed. When the patient mentioned the doctor who operated on him, his uncle, his girl, his parents and the policeman who surprised him with the girl, the colon reacted by increased hyperæmia, contraction, discharge of fæces through the stoma and secretion of mucus which, after the 50th minute of the interview, was blood-streaked.

Fig. 22

It was possible, by means of long conversations with him about his social life, work and home conditions, to correlate the colour, size and state of his colonic mucous membrane with that of the topic of conversation. During periods of silence the colour of the mucous membrane would gradually get a deeper red and the opening would contract. At the same time he would show increasing signs of tension and anxiety. A few moments after the silence was broken by some question about his illness, the redness would diminish and the size become stabilised and colonic activity in general would become less. Various neutral subjects such as a discussion of his hobbies would also produce a similar effect. Any attempt to introduce the subject of his girl friend with whom he was having a secret love affair disapproved of by his father, produced marked redness, colonic peristalsis and even bleeding of the mucous membrane. It is a common observation that hostility, frustration and conflict of this type can produce marked clinical attacks of ulcerative colitis (Fig. 22). There is also little doubt that the converse is true. Alteration in the environment of the patient which reduces the amount of frustration and conflict, can and does sometimes produce " spontaneous " remissions in the patient's condition. Although psychological factors play such an important part in the aetiology of this condition, it must not be taken that psychotherapy is necessarily the best means of treatment. Here again a multifactorial approach is indicated. The fluid balance of the body must be preserved, any loss of blood replaced directly or indirectly, cortisone used to lessen the inflammation and if necessary surgery to prevent the colon's becoming neoplastic. Many cases would also benefit from a sympathetic psychological approach in which the patients' difficulties and conflicts were sorted out.

SELECTED BIBLIOGRAPHY

1. *The Varieties of Human Physique.* Sheldon, W. H. 1940. London: Harper.
2. *Psychological Aspects of Clinical Medicine.* Barton Hall, S. 1949. London: H. K. Lewis.

Chapter 12

ORIENTATION AND DISORIENTATION

Psychological Orientation

Just as the pilot of an aeroplane must have correct bearings to enable him to stay on his course, to alter course wisely in case of difficulty or danger, and to reach his destination in safety and good time, so every human being needs " bearings " of a particular kind if he is to function effectively and adapt his behaviour to changing circumstances. " Psychological Orientation " is the term we use to describe the bearings by which we steer our course in everyday life, and the reliability of these bearings may vary from time to time, even in health. In diseased states of mind or body, or both, orientation may fail partly or completely, and a patient in such a condition is said to be " disorientated ".

Dimensions of Orientation

To be fully orientated we must have readily available two sets of information: about ourselves and about our environment.

Information about Ourselves

The pilot might have excellent maps, navigating instruments, full meteorological information and radar equipment, but if he did not know what sort of aeroplane he was handling he could still make fatal mistakes. We must know who we are for correct orientation. Self-awareness implies knowledge of one's name, sex, age, date of birth, address, occupation and so on. It must also include accurate estimation of one's abilities and disabilities, with consequent power to distinguish between efficient and inefficient, sensible and reckless courses of action. Even the simpler levels of self-awareness can be lost in severe psychological and organic disorders.

Information about the Environment

Where we are. We must know where we are, so that we can be correctly " orientated for place ". Waking in a strange bedroom on the first morning of a holiday provides a common experience of disorientation for place which is brief but can nevertheless be highly disturbing. Delirious patients commonly fail to recognise places in which they find themselves.

Bodily posture. We must grasp where we are ourselves in relation to our surroundings. That is, we must know whether we are sitting, standing or lying down; then we are correctly " orientated for posture ". We must also be " topographically orientated " so that our surroundings and our bodies are in sensible relation to each other: postural orientation is in fact closely linked with our appreciation of the layout of our immediate environment, and when flying blind in total darkness, or in cloud, an aeroplane pilot readily becomes confused about his position. He may be convinced that he is flying on his side, or upside down, until he learns that his instruments are more reliable guides than his own sense of position. If we have come into a room by a door, we must know where that door is when we leave, and distinguish this door from cupboard doors. A topographically disorientated patient may find himself perplexed when it comes to finding and opening a door. In a hospital ward he may fail to locate his own bed, or the correct route to the bathroom. We must be aware of the arrangement and of the approximate dimensions of our bodies in space; this is " spatial orientation ". The failure of spatial awareness, which occurs in some types of cortical brain disease, leads to gross mistakes such as damaging an outstretched arm by failing to realise that it will not pass through a doorway without being brought down to the side of the body.

What the time is. We must know what the time is. " Temporal orientation " need not be exact, but in most urban and industrial communities we feel at a loss and behave inefficiently if we are not sure of the time to within an hour or so. We need to know the day of the week, the date of the month and the year, in order to behave appropriately: and all this knowledge can be lost if it is made to seem unimportant, as it may do in many kinds of institutional depersonalised life where one day is the same as the other. Patients in badly run hospitals, aged people in institutions, and prisoners in solitary confinement tend to lose their power to differentiate one day from the rest. The absence of time clues such as clocks, calendars, diaries, newspapers, and radio and television programmes makes it difficult to assess hours and dates; but out of doors other time clues are given by the position of the sun, the length of the shadows, and the alternation of day and night. Seasonal changes also help us to find our rough bearings in time. Once again, the chronic patient confined indoors loses many of these sources of temporal orientation, and the slight variation between meals or the changes in ward routine may be his only means of differentiating one part of the day from the other.

Recognition of people. We need to recognise people we know, and conversely to be aware that strangers are strangers when we see them.

This ability is termed " orientation for persons ". Calling people by their wrong names is common in organic states of confusion, and so is the failure to recognise well-known friends and relations.

Significance of events. We must have some understanding of the significance of events that are taking place about us, and this ability to comprehend is closely linked with orientation for persons: we tend to recognise people by the way they behave. Our own behaviour cannot be appropriate if we misinterpret the behaviour of others. A stranger might mistake a friendly fight between brothers as a murderous assault, and so be led to intervene with more violence than the situation demanded, whereas a neighbour who could recognise the boys and grasp the nature of their fight might well decide to leave well alone. It is important to notice here that the stranger has acted correctly according to his lights; but the bearings he took were inadequate, his appreciation of the significance of the events he witnessed was not correct and therefore he could not choose the right course of action. We might say that his judgment was incorrect.

Reality and fantasy. We must be able to distinguish between reality and fantasy. To carry out ordinary daily tasks it is essential that we should be able to distinguish what is really happening to us at the moment from what we would like to believe is happening (or what we fear might be happening), or from past events. Confused people cannot effectively make this distinction. Their fantasies and memories may even take visible shape or become audible, as visual and auditory hallucinations.

Essential Factors in Achieving Orientation

Consciousness

We cannot know who or where we are, or anything at all, without being in a conscious state, and the more alert we are the more likely we are to be properly orientated. We are more likely to be alert if we are interested in our surroundings, unfatigued, and not distracted by intense emotion or pain, or preoccupied with a limited number of obtrusive thoughts.

Adequate Sensory Stimulation

This factor naturally falls into three categories:

(i) *The sensory barrage.* Sensory stimulation provided by the outside world and arising from one's own body must be provided as the raw material of experience.

(ii) *Sensation.* The sensory apparatus and the afferent nervous pathways must be functioning correctly so as to conduct sensory signals to the brain.

(iii) *Perception.* The brain must be able to interpret incoming signals from the sensory apparatus promptly and correctly, and, by reference to its store of memories of past perceptions, make a meaningful perceptual pattern out of the sensory barrage (Fig. 23).

Adequate Experience, Memory and Learning Ability

We must be able rapidly to relate new sensations and events to our past experience if we are to make accurate analyses and sound judgments on which to base our reactions. Again we can only be properly orientated if we can grasp and retain perceptions as soon as they are presented. For instance, to be adequately orientated for time we must be able to remember what we saw on the clock when we looked at it, and we must be able to retain the memory of the name of the street or building we are in if we are to be correctly orientated for place.

Adequate Powers of Communication

We depend very much on other people to help us find our bearings. We can ask for information provided that we can speak intelligibly, and we can make use of what information is given us provided that we can hear and understand what we are told. These skills of communication extend of course to gesture, writing and reading, as well as speech.

Psychological Disorientation

A great deal of our knowledge about correct orientation is derived from the study of people who are inadequately aware of, or are mistaken about, their surroundings and experiences. Such people are described clinically as being " disorientated or confused ". Confusional states associated with organic disease, and particularly with toxic states and fever, are commonly found in " deliria " (singular: delirium). A confusional state may begin acutely and dramatically, or develop so slowly and insidiously that it becomes very difficult to decide when the patient ceased to be able to behave in a normal manner. The degree of confusion in any one patient tends to vary from one hour to another, and often there are phases of adequate orientation which interrupt the confusional state from time to time.

We cannot make an absolutely clear cut-and-dried classification of either the causes or the varieties of confusional disorder. The condition never exists in isolation; its occurrence is linked with other disturbances of mental and physical function, and its manifestations may be modified by an enormous range of factors, some of which will be considered below. The list of causes that follow contains many overlapping and recurring factors which may contribute to the patient's total disability, and which cannot be artificially separated from the clinical picture of a

Schematic Diagram of Factors Contributing to Normal Perception: The Basis of Correct Orientation

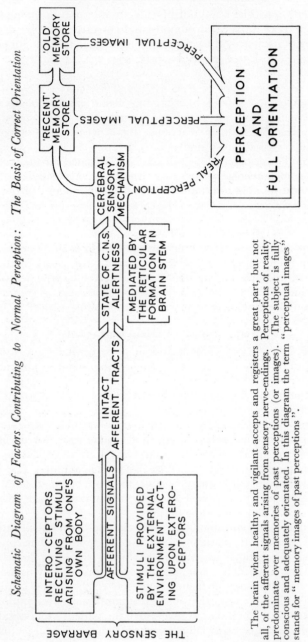

Fig. 23

The brain when healthy and vigilant accepts and registers a great part, but not all, of the afferent signals arising from sensory nerve-endings. Perceptions of reality predominate over memories of past perceptions (or images). The subject is fully conscious and adequately orientated. In this diagram the term " perceptual images " stands for " memory images of past perceptions ".

whole human being in a recognisable state of disordered perception and consequent disorientation. It might be interesting and useful to determine in each of the following clinical causes of disorientation those factors already described as being essential for achieving orientation, which are diminished or absent. It will soon become plain that many such factors are involved in each condition.

Causes of Disorientation

Extremes of Youth and Old Age

Very young children, that is infants and toddlers, cannot help but be very inadequately orientated, although the extent of their disorientation diminishes with maturation, growth of intelligence and experience. They are never fully aware of their own identity, and, apart from members of their own family, cannot recognise the identity of other people. They only know where they are in a few familiar places and soon become extremely puzzled and even distressed when put in unfamiliar surroundings. They have no access to the usual orientating clues to time and place; their powers of requesting, giving or receiving information are very limited, and their inexperience and inadequate understanding combine to make small children uncertain as to the significance of events happening about them.

Old people lose grasp of their situation very readily. Failing sight and hearing result in imperfect and inadequate sensory stimulation, and in social isolation caused by being deprived of visual and auditory means of communication. A failing memory for recent events and a diminished ability to learn new material contribute to a loss of bearings in everyday life. Cerebral degeneration accompanying old age is another factor, and loneliness, poverty and infirmity, by reducing their daily contacts with other people or with books, radio, television and newspapers, all increase their disorientation. The impersonal and monotonous regime of an institution all too often completes the process.

Drowsiness, Sleep and Sleep Deprivation

In all these states we experience periods of confusion accompanied by vivid hallucinations: when we are in fact dreaming. Prolonged loss of sleep, experimentally or sometimes punitively induced, leads to unavoidable drowsing, and in this kind of light sleep hallucinatory dream experiences will occur. Sleep-walking (somnambulism) is the translation of the dream experience into action. The probable mechanism of dream-disorientation is suggested in the following diagram, which should be compared with the schematic outline of the processes of normal perception and orientation, given earlier in this chapter (Fig. 24).

Lack of Adequate Sensory Stimulation (Sensory Deprivation)

Darkness and silence acting separately or together are potent causes of disorientation even in healthy subjects, and if prolonged can lead to hallucinosis. Loneliness and boredom have a milder effect. The four are combined in solitary confinement and may also occur when sick people, especially the very old or the very young, are left alone for lengthy periods in a darkened room at night.

Failures of sensory receptor mechanisms can operate in the same way, and people who become rapidly or instantaneously deaf or blind, and have no opportunity to make adjustments necessary for their suddenly altered state, may become seriously disorientated for a time. Those who have been blindfolded in a party game or lost in a thick fog, will appreciate the confusion, terror and despair of the person who is truly disabled by being deprived of his major sources of sensory information.

Disorders of Cerebral Metabolism, Nutrition and Function

Pyrexia. Fever, especially in sick children, is a common cause of delirium, and as the temperature of the body returns to normal so the confusion tends to clear. Even without infection being present, a simple rise of body temperature as in heat-stroke, can result in disorientation.

Toxic states. These divide naturally into those caused by poisons administered intentionally or unintentionally (exogenous toxins) and those manufactured within the body (endogenous toxins). *Exogenous toxins* causing delirium include general anaesthetics, hypnotic drugs such as barbiturate preparations and ethyl alcohol (one notorious confusional state associated with chronic alcoholic poisoning is known as " delirium tremens "); deliriant drugs such as mescaline and derivatives of cannabis indica; atropine and morphine in susceptible persons, heavy metals such as lead and mercury; carbon monoxide and other gaseous poisons. *Endogenous toxins* are produced in many metabolic disorders, including failure of kidney function (uraemia), of the liver (cholaemia), and in the state of ketosis in diabetes mellitus. In these conditions delirium commonly precedes coma and death, if treatment is not available. Toxins are also manufactured in the tissues or blood stream by pathogenic organisms (in states of toxaemia) and this cause of delirium is often seen in acute streptococcal infections of the tonsil and middle ear, in staphylococcal osteomyelitis, and in bacterial pneumonia. These infections are commonly accompanied by pyrexia

Schematic diagram of factors contributing to disorientation

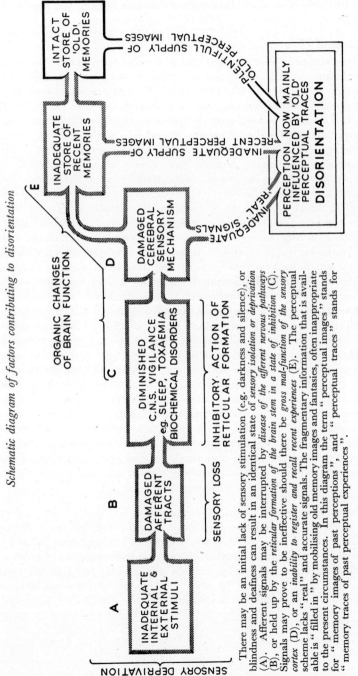

Fig. 24

There may be an initial lack of sensory stimulation (e.g. darkness and silence), or blindness and deafness can result in an identical state of *sensory isolation or deprivation* (A). Afferent signals may be interrupted by *disease of the afferent nervous pathways* (B), or held up by the *reticular formation of the brain stem in a state of inhibition* (C). Signals may prove to be ineffective should there be *gross mal-function of the sensory cortex* (D), or an *inability to register and recall recent experiences* (E). The perceptual scheme lacks "real" and accurate signals. The fragmentary information that is available is "filled in" by mobilising old memory images and fantasies, often inappropriate to the present circumstances. In this diagram the term "perceptual images" stands for "memory images of past perceptions", and "perceptual traces" stands for "memory traces of past perceptual experiences".

but virus infections may also produce delirium even in the absence of high fever.

Biochemical Disorders of the Blood and Tissue Fluids

These comprise a very mixed group of disorders which do not occur in isolation. Thus, *dehydration* accompanies many severe infections, metabolic disorders and also heat-stroke. *Electrolyte imbalance* commonly accompanies severe burns, vomiting, diarrhoea and dehydration; *changes in the pH of the blood* occur with a wide range of cardio-respiratory, gastro-intestinal, renal and hepatic disorders; inadequate concentration of glucose in the blood (hypoglycaemia) results from insulin poisoning or starvation. *Hypoxia* may occur with severe anaemia, at high altitudes, during incorrectly administered general anaesthesia, and in cardio-respiratory disorders. Gross deficiency of vitamins of the B-complex, as in pellagra, may provoke disorientation. In all these states cerebral metabolism is interfered with, and as a consequence psychological functioning becomes faulty, perception is interfered with, and confusion may develop. Interestingly enough we can obtain convincing, if indirect, evidence of the disordered state of cerebral metabolism in such disorientated patients; a very high proportion display gross electro-encephalographic* abnormalities.

Damage and disease of brain tissue. Confusion may occur in conditions which result in actual physical damage to the brain, such as concussion and cerebral laceration, or infective illness like meningo-encephalitis. Cerebral degenerations, especially in senility, are a common cause of disorientation and these are frequently associated with interference with the cerebro-vascular circulation as in cerebral thrombosis, haemorrhage and embolism. Tumours and abscesses of the brain can destroy cerebral tissue, or interfere with cerebral metabolism, and so cause delirium. Episodes of disorientation commonly occur in the course of epilepsy; the electro-encephalographic recordings reveal the major electro-physiological abnormalities that are at the roots of this category of organic dysfunction of the central nervous system.

Schizophrenic Illness

The schizophrenic patient has been said to be " a dreamer " asleep in a world awake, and this description would cover the severe degree of disorientation met with in some types of schizophrenic disorder. It seems likely that schizophrenic illnesses are manifestations of cerebral metabolic disorders as yet imperfectly understood, and that the time will come when we shall be able to cure or control schizophrenic illness by suitable biochemical treatment.

---

* See Glossary

The Characteristics of Disorientated Behaviour

These may vary greatly from patient to patient, and from time to time in any one patient, and this variability in the one patient is in itself a characteristic of disorientation. From what we have already said of the role played by the sensory barrage in contributing both to alertness and to correct perceptions, it is easy to realise that darkness, silence and loneliness will tend to exacerbate the symptoms: toxic confusional states such as delirium tremens often first show themselves during the hours of darkness. Deliberate, sensible and kind efforts to stimulate and reassure the confused patient may reduce the extent of his disorientation by making him more aware of his real situation.

The disorientated subject will generally act in a manner that is fully consistent with his own distorted and inadequate appreciation of the environment and of himself, but, apart from the difficulties of attempting to navigate while using faulty data, the patient's behaviour is also affected by other psychological changes which often accompany disordered cerebral functioning. These may be diminished consciousness, slow thinking, memory defects, loss of self-control, deterioration in skills of all kinds and disordered mood.

He may mistake his bearings in time, place and space. He may identify people incorrectly. He may misinterpret the evidence given him by his senses; in other words he may have *illusions*, and may perceive a flower-patterned wallpaper as a host of ugly faces menacing him, or wrongly recognise a nurse as being his mother. When sensory stimuli fail to give him sufficient perceptual data on which to act, he calls up images from his memory. Self-derived perceptual experiences are called *autochthonous*; and when they are experienced by the patient as being completely " real ", that is the perceptions appear to be originating from present happenings, we say the patient is experiencing *hallucinations*. He may also form mistaken beliefs, usually founded upon illusory and hallucinated perceptions, which cannot be easily abolished by any demonstrations of their palpable absurdity, and these are called *delusions*. He may be positive that his nurse is his long dead mother, and no rational argument will alter this conviction.

He may tend to live in the past rather than in the " here " and " now ", and will often regard a new experience as a repetition of something old and familiar. Many illusory experiences and delusional beliefs may be based on this fundamental inability to appreciate reality, which can occur in healthy people at times of intolerable stress or heightened emotion, as in extreme states of exhaustion, fear and grief.

He may exhibit a lower level of consciousness than is normal, and may be obviously drowsy, and unresponsive to the external world.

It may be very hard to establish any sort of contact with a patient who can only be roused for short periods. Abnormal electro-encephalographic changes are often present when consciousness is reduced.

His memory may be poor, especially for recent events. He may grasp information that is given him slowly and inaccurately, and then cannot long retain what he has been told. When he is aware of his defective memory, he may invent material to fill the gaps. He is then said to " confabulate ".

His emotional state can change rapidly from apathy to cheerfulness, and from cheerfulness to depression. He may be aware of his " emotional lability " but be unable to control his expression of feeling. He will often display anxiety, and this may worsen so that he presents a picture of absolute dread, terror or even panic.

His general level of behaviour deteriorates. On the one hand he may go back to the outgrown modes of his childhood, feed himself messily, wet and soil his clothing, and display temper tantrums. This impairment of skills acquired through maturation and social training is termed *regression* (see Chapter 8). On the other hand he may openly do things that normal adults in public refrain from doing by conscious effort. He may shout abuse, sing loudly, pass flatus noisily or masturbate shamelessly. We then say he is "disinhibited". Regression and disinhibition usually go together: both result from a loss of mature powers of self-control and social awareness.

His speech will often be disordered, rambling, repetitive, and full of puns, rhymes and bizarre associations; like a spoken commentary to a dream. He may condense words together, or he may omit key words or even whole sentences and so be impossible to understand. Or he may use words that have no meaning to anyone but himself: his own jargon.

His level of performance in formal psychological tests is generally very poor. He cannot attend for long, is easily distracted and probably has very little interest in the test situation. He thinks slowly, is easily tired, cannot understand instructions or recall information given him only a few minutes before. Old skills that have been long established show least deterioration; he may score well in tests of vocabulary and general information or those that involve rote learning such as simple arithmetical calculation. New problems are badly done, and his capacity to classify or to think in abstract terms is very limited. If he is asked to explain the everyday proverb "look before you leap" he will reduce it to a piece of concrete advice: " you will get wet if you don't ". " Every cloud has a silver lining " is interpreted as " clouds look like silver: well, the edges anyway" (see Chapter 3).

Conclusion

Disorientation in sick people is not uncommon, nor is it hard to recognise in its grosser manifestations. Everyone of us in his dreams is in a state closely resembling delirium: remembrance of the panic and misery produced by some dreams should enable us to feel real sympathy for the confused patient in his lonely and perplexing world of disordered perception.

SELECTED BIBLIOGRAPHY

1. *Sleeping and Waking*. Oswald, I. 1962. Amsterdam and New York: Elsevier.
   A comprehensive account of neuro-physiological mechanisms that are thought to be involved in correct orientation, and well-written accounts of disorientation produced by forced lack of sleep, and accompanying various states of altered consciousness.
2. *The Snake Pit*. Ward, M. J. 1946. New York: Random House.
   A moving account, possibly first hand, of a prolonged confusional illness.

Chapter 13

SLEEP

The day's activity in man and most of the higher animals is subject to a cyclical pattern in which we can recognise two definite components, *wakefulness* and *sleep*, and a borderline state of *fatigue* or drowsiness occurring whenever one gives place to the other.

In *wakefulness* all our senses are alert, our body movements are vigorous and purposeful, our reaction times are at their briefest; we have good control over our emotions, we can learn new facts and recall at will those we have previously learned. We are firmly in touch with our real circumstances and talk and act in a way that shows us to be competent in handling our affairs.

When we are fatigued there is a general deterioration in all these powers and processes; from fatigue we pass into a twilight state between sleeping and waking, usually called drowsiness, which in turn gives way to sleep.

This cyclical variation in activity is innate, not learned. Man and his domestic animals, as well as many animals in the wild state, have discovered a variety of ways of making sleep come more easily; most of these methods of inducing sleep involve a deliberate reduction in the stimuli acting on our sense organs and tending therefore to demand some sort of reaction. In general, when we want to sleep we look for darkness and quiet, and cover ourselves warmly to reduce changes in the thermal and tactile stimuli acting on our skin. Experimentally it has been shown that isolation in a chamber where stimuli are reduced to an absolute minimum by insulation against sound and temperature changes and absence of light and air currents, induces sleep in man, and Pavlov's dogs often fell asleep when held still in firm harness in a darkened room. Thus sleep is encouraged by conditions of sensory deprivation. Monotonous, repetitive, stimuli sometimes induce sleep; the sound of a train's wheels lulls many passengers and " counting sheep " is one of a variety of rituals used to encourage sleep. Sleep can also come swiftly after intense mental or physical fatigue, or an emotional crisis, and vigorous outdoor exercise is well known as a promoter of a good night's sleep.

But even when all these conditions favouring sleep are absent, or are present continuously, wakefulness, drowsing and sleep still occur. A man who spends many hours in conditions of sensory deprivation,

tends to drowse and sleep for long periods but all the same he does not
sleep all the time. Crustacea living in deep, lightless, underground
caves where the environment remains constant throughout the day,
the seasons and for millenia of man's time, still show behaviour
conforming to a rhythmic pattern, resembling our own cycle of
waking and sleeping.

Control of Sleep/Waking Rhythm

The inborn mechanism that regulates this pattern of waxing and
waning activity is probably situated in the *reticular formation*, a mass
of neurones and nerve fibres which occupies the central core of the
brain stem from the thalamus to the medulla, and communicates
with every part of the cerebral cortex (except the visual areas), and
with the spinal cord (see Chapter 6).

The evidence for this location of function has been derived from
experiments on decorticate animals; such animals once they have
recovered from the operation continue to sleep and wake, even if the
sensory tracts in the brain stem are also permanently divided: this
indicates that cortical activity and afferent stimuli reaching the cortex
are not essential for maintaining the sleep/waking rhythm. But if
electrodes are implanted in the reticular formation of the mesencephalon of these animals, electrical stimulation will awaken them from
sleep, or increase their alertness if they are already awake; while
stimulation applied to the lower reticular formation between the pons
and the medulla will produce drowsiness or sleep.

In man and animals in the natural state, the reticular formation is
activated by afferent stimuli from the internal and external sensory
organs, by efferent stimuli from the cortex, and by humoral influences
such as circulating adrenaline and noradrenaline. States of acidosis
and the administration of drugs of the amphetamine type also stimulate
the reticular formation and rouse the subject; the change is reflected
in the electro-encephalogram:*   there are distinct wave shapes
associated with full wakefulness, drowsing, light and deep sleep.

The reticular formation is *inhibited* by warmth, by the action of
hypnotic drugs (such as the derivatives of barbituric acid) and by
stimuli arising from the stretch receptors in the carotid sinus and the
arch of the aorta. There is evidence that during sleep the cerebral
cortex and spinal cord still deliver stimuli to the reticular formation
but that these are blocked at this level and therefore fail to produce
effective action.

---

* See Glossary.

Besides these external factors influencing the activity of the reticular formation, there is an internal variation in the excitability of the neurones of which it is composed; this is well shown in decorticate animals. The variation is itself rhythmical, and can be thought of as underlying and determining the response made by the individual to the same type of stimulus at different periods in the cycle. Once the reticular formation has passed into its inhibitory phase, then afferent stimuli which would normally produce increased alertness in the individual will prove much less effective in overcoming his drowsiness.

The Physical Concomitants of Sleep

Body movements are reduced or absent in sleep, especially in the first hours; the tonus of voluntary muscle is correspondingly reduced, tendon reflexes are diminished or absent, and the plantar response becomes extensor in type. The body sphincters are often said actually to increase in tone, but this is probably not so; men can and do sleep with their eyes and mouths open. Defaecation and micturition are nevertheless inhibited in the mature, healthy human, and the pupils of the eyes are constricted. There is a fall in blood pressure, in the pulse and respiratory rate, and in the rate of secretion of urine, and metabolism becomes truly basal. The body temperature tends to fall, and there is a mild hypoxia and acidosis.

Pre-Scientific Explanations of Sleep

Throughout the ages sleep has been equated with death; it has seemed to be a state of total, if reversible, cessation of all bodily and mental activity. A rich treasury of quotations could be assembled around the metaphorical linkage between sleep and health; most would undoubtedly represent the efforts of poets to make the idea of death a little more bearable by reducing death to a night's repose:

> " The worse than can befall thee, measur'd right,
> Is a sound slumber and a long good night."
>
> (Dryden: translating Lucretius)

But there are poems that point the opposite conclusion:

> " New ev'ry morning is the love
> Our wakening and uprising prove:
> Through sleep and darkness safely brought,
> Restor'd to life and power and thought."
>
> (J. Keble)

Children, like poets, often think of sleep as a kind of death, and " Pussy's gone to sleep for ever and ever " when the family pet dies is an everyday illustration of the usefulness of this simple concept.

Primitive people take the belief a stage further and sometimes think that the soul leaves the body during sleep, and the body so left vacant may become the host for other minds or even for occupation by gods or demons. Widespread in all age groups and vastly different cultures is the assumption that sleeping and waking are radically opposed states of behaviour.

In the circumstances, the equally universal assumption that sleep is good, indeed essential for the health of mind and body, may be seen to represent a victory for man's powers of observation and deduction over his inclination to superstitious terror in the face of what is difficult to understand. Macbeth is afraid to die, but he longs for sleep.

Sleep as an Activity

Sleep becomes less mysterious if we discard the concept of its total difference from the waking state and look instead at the evidence for its being a specialised form of individual activity in which attention to the environment is greatly reduced, or even absent. Here are some of the observed facts on which this view can be based.

1. Body movements persist, especially those designed to protect the sleeper.

2. The cerebral blood flow is actually increased during sleep.

3. The parasympathetic nervous system is active throughout sleeping hours; its outflow then predominates over the sympathetic.

4. Intellectual and emotional problems can be solved during sleep (see Chapter 3).

5. Recently learned material is efficiently memorised during sleep, if only because there has been no " interference " by other learning processes during the time we have been asleep, thus making it possible for consolidation of the memory to take place (see Chapter 4).

6. The apparent inattention of the sleeper is selective, not indiscriminate. A mother will wake instantly when her baby cries, but sleeps through the noise of traffic in the street outside, or the sound of the telephone which rouses her doctor-husband. Most people are roused by the smell of gas escaping, or of burning, or by unfamiliar noises in the house; jet planes screaming overhead are usually ignored once the sleeper has got used to them.

7. Hallucinations are quite common in healthy people both in sleep itself and in the state between sleeping and waking, when they are sometimes so intense as to convince the sleeper of their reality. He is sure he heard somebody calling; he is certain he went downstairs to put the cat out. While asleep his hallucinations showed themselves in his talking or muttering, in tooth-grinding (especially common in

children) sometimes even in gross body movements such as sitting up, or getting out of bed to walk around the room. This sleeper is acting out his dreams while sleep walking.

8. Epileptic subjects are sometimes sent into a convulsion or its equivalent when drowsing or asleep, although they may be completely free from epileptic attacks when they are alert and vigilant.

9. It is at least arguable that some forms of enuresis (bed-wetting) represent not an automatic voiding of the contents of the full bladder during deep sleep but a semi-voluntary act in a state of light sleep, perhaps accompanied by dreams of swimming, immersion or actual urination.

Factors Influencing the Rhythm of Sleep and Wakefulness in Man

The Age of the Sleeper

The newborn baby drowses nearly all the time, waking only to be fed. After a few weeks, he is obviously awake for longer periods, and always if he is hungry, cold, uncomfortable or wanting loving attention from his mother. Conversely he sleeps soundly when he is warm, replete, dry and especially if he is also securely held by warm arms or blankets and rhythmically lulled by rocking movements. By three or four months he will demand some social life during his waking periods; either his mother or some gay, moving toy will keep him happy and alert. At a year old he will sleep most of the night, with luck and good management, and probably require a sleep of two to three hours' duration during the morning or the afternoon, the so-called daytime nap. Western European children, in a culture which favours privacy for the parents during the husband's leisure hours, are generally sent to bed in the early evening after the age of three and then cease to need a daytime period of sleep. Most children accept and thrive on this pattern and it then persists throughout adult life with a suitable adjustment of the actual time of going to bed. With old age a change occurs, perhaps reinforced by the lack of a definite time-table of work and relaxation such as the working man and woman must observe. The very old drowse frequently during the daylight hours and tend to sleep for shorter periods at night; they often wake very early and find the hours before breakfast very trying (Fig. 25).

The Alternation of Night and Day

It is convenient for most people in most places to sleep and wake at similar hours. In the Polar regions where the alternation of light and darkness is seasonal rather than diurnal, custom dictates that the late post-meridional and early ante-meridional hours are the ones to be spent in bed.

Almost certainly this is only a matter of habit or convenience; night shift workers can and do sleep in the daytime; and usually if they dislike this arrangement they dislike it because they cannot sleep when the rest of the community is awake.

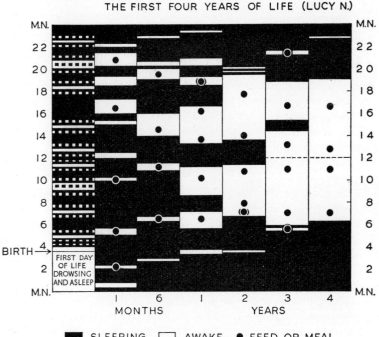

CHART: SLEEP / WAKING / FEEDING PATTERNS IN THE FIRST FOUR YEARS OF LIFE (LUCY N.)

■ SLEEPING   ▢ AWAKE   ● FEED OR MEAL

◉ OCCASIONAL FEED OR MEAL

As the child grows older, the wakeful periods extend and coalesce. By the age of 4 years Lucy has given up her afternoon nap, and her meal-times and her waking and sleeping phases have become grouped together so as to be socially convenient. She can go for as much as 14 hours during the night without a meal, so that sleep is only once disturbed at about 11 p.m. by her need to pass urine.

Fig. 25

Individual Differences

Different people vary very greatly in the amount of sleep they need, and perhaps even more in the amount they personally think desirable.

If all social influences are removed, men tend to sleep in shorter, broken periods, but the total number of hours spent asleep in every twenty-four-hour period is almost constant for each individual. Lewis and Masterson reported that twenty-nine men on a British North Greenland expedition (1952–54) each slept an average of 7.9 hours a day almost irrespective of the season and of bodily activity. Apart from having to carry out essential scientific duties and domestic chores, these men could sleep when they wished and a minimum of social sanctions were imposed upon them.

Physical and Mental Illness

Pain is tiring and leads to general fatigue but rarely permits a deep refreshing sleep. Some types of sudden acute pain lead to immediate waking, a typical instance being the pain of a diseased joint which becomes intense as muscle guarding relaxes during sleep and inflamed surfaces come into contact with each other.

Toxic states may be accompanied by drowsiness, but sometimes produce severe insomnia.

Disease or damage to the mesencephalon and diencephalon produces drowsiness with pathological episodes of deep sleep. During the years immediately after the first world war, when there was a world-wide epidemic of virus encephalitis, many patients during and after convalescence had gross abnormalities of sleep/waking rhythm, and it was often thought that the post-encephalitic subject tended to slumber during the daytime and be wakeful at night. This apparent reversal of the normal sleep/waking rhythm may have been the result of inaccurate observation. It might have been that these patients were slumbering and waking in a fitful fashion throughout the twenty-four hours. The uncommon disorder known as *narcolepsy* results in the patient's dropping off into deep sleep even in the absence of any premonitory drowsiness, and narcolepsy is probably the result of damage in the region of the diencephalon.

Severe anxiety and catastrophic emotional outbursts often lead to wakefulness or disturbed light sleep with much dreaming; but there are some people who actually sleep longer and more deeply in these conditions.

The insomnia of severe depressive illnesses has a characteristic pattern: the patient will usually say " I can't get off till midnight, then I wake about 4 a.m. and can't get back to sleep ". This is called *initial* and *terminal insomnia*, and the terminal phase is in fact the more significant.

The Effects of Prolonged Sleep Deprivation

Berger and Oswald (1962) studied six male medical students who were deprived of sleep for a total of 108 hours each, day and night. Their subjects displayed the following phenomena:

Fatigue with napping.
Physical clumsiness.
An inability to concentrate on, or perform, everyday tasks with ordinary efficiency.
Intrusive thoughts, passing on to illusions and actual visual, aural and somatic hallucinations.
Bizarre use of words, and the manufacture of new words (neologisms).
Bizarre motor behaviour.
Delusory beliefs.
Failure to discriminate between reality and fantasy.

In general, these young men seemed to be in a state of fluctuating confusion with drowsiness, very similar to the mental state of patients in toxic delirium, or suffering from schizophrenia. (These states are described in more detail in Chapter 12.) They behaved " as if in a waking dream ".

Experimental work of this kind is necessarily limited in scope and intention, but in fact prolonged sleep deprivation may lead to fatal exhaustion. Minor degrees in ordinary life lead to depression, anxiety, inefficiency and a marked decline in emotional self-control. Sleepless children are in actual physical danger from their sleep-deprived parents; adults who are unable to rest in the daytime lose their resourcefulness and resilience, become irritable, hostile and prone to outbursts of aggression. Before this is dismissed as an exaggerated statement, some newspaper accounts should be read of the injuries and deaths of babies and very young children who have been assaulted by chronically sleep-deprived parents; a substantial number of suicides by young mothers with or without accompanying destruction of their children are also at least partially to be accounted for by the severe strain of prolonged sleeplessness; and family doctors and children's physicians are nowadays well aware of the vicious circle initiated by a screaming baby and critical neighbours, followed by failure of lactation on the part of the exhausted mother, followed by more screaming as the baby's hunger increases, followed by a terrible sense of inadequacy on the part of the mother which predisposes her to further insomnia. This type of common problem should never be lightly dismissed; it may not lead to a homicidal attack or a suicidal attempt but it can poison the relationships within the family for months or years, perhaps occasionally for ever.

Depth of Sleep

Electro-encephalographic records, measurements of general body movement and observations on responsiveness to such stimuli as noise, touch, pinching and pinprick, show that sleep is usually deepest during the first few hours. Even in deep early sleep stimuli are perceived though in a selected manner; later in sleep the mobility of the body increases and the sleeper becomes progressively easier to waken, passing more rapidly from torpor to a state of physical alertness and awareness of reality. If a sleeper is roused during a phase of deep sleep he will often remain confused, drowsy and physically inco-ordinated for some time.

Twilight Sleep

A variety of sensory and motor phenomena accompany that state of drowsiness when a man is neither fully asleep nor fully awake, a phase often called " twilight sleep ", which tends to occur at the beginning and end of natural sleep. (This should not be confused with the stupefied condition produced during childbirth by the use of morphia and its derivatives: a procedure that came into fashion in the 1920s, proved to be very dangerous and is now completely discredited.)

These phenomena are commonly termed " hypnagogic ", and are often unpleasant and accompanied by feelings of alarm and helplessness, but some fortunate people actually enjoy hypnagogic changes and like to linger in the twilight phase.

Sensory changes often take the form of hallucinatory experiences— that is to say, the sleeper has perceptual experiences, although no stimuli are in fact being applied to the peripheral sense organs. It is common to hear bells ringing, raps on the door, twanging, (as if a stringed instrument were being plucked), or shouts and summoning cries. Visual hallucinations may include flashing lights, geometric patterns, animal or human figures. Tactile hallucinations are less frequent but some subjects feel as if they are being pressed upon, prodded or swarmed over by insects or animals. Misinterpretations of real stimuli gives rise to " illusions "; for instance, the drowsing man's changing awareness of his posture may cause hypnagogic sensations of falling, while faulty awareness of his body image may cause him to think that part of his body is shrinking or expanding.

Motor phenomena occurring in the hypnagogic state are more limited in range; jerking, moaning and muttering are common, and waking with a jerk is often associated with the sleeper's belief that he has fallen. There is a phenomenon known as " sleep paralysis " in which the subject is apparently alert but cannot move in spite of wishing to:

this may be another aspect of the motor anomalies belonging to the hypnagogic state, notably in the change from light sleep to sudden arousal.

Both sensory and motor phenomena of the hypnagogic state tend to be fairly constant for the individual. They frequently occur during and after toxic illnesses with accompanying nightmares and delirium; one subject during the delirium of measles became convinced that the walls and ceiling of his bedroom were receding at great speed. This feeling, with its concomitant terror, recurred over several years when he was in the hypnagogic state. Usually the sleeper retains some awareness of the unreal nature of his experiences; the basic nature of " twilight sleep " suggests that hypnagogic phenomena are in fact brief dreams occurring while the dreamer is still in partial or intermittent touch with reality. Oswald has rather neatly described hypnagogic states as " micro-dreams ".

Dreaming and Dreams

Physiological Aspects of Dreaming

Of recent years much valuable research has been directed to the physical concomitants of dreaming by such workers as Aserinsky, Kleitman, Dement, Oswald and Berger. It is now fairly certain that dreaming is mainly associated with light sleep and drowsing; it is known to be accompanied by rapid synchronous eye movements in sighted people (as if they were in fact looking at real objects and actions), the heart and respiratory rates increase, phonation may occur, and bodily movements increase. Oswald describes characteristic sawtoothed wave activity in electro-encephalographic recordings made while the subject was dreaming. It seems that sleep is regularly punctuated at intervals of about an hour and a half by phases of lighter sleep laden with dreams. These dream periods may last only a few minutes, but sometimes extend to half an hour or more. Oswald estimates that about 90 minutes of an average adult's night sleep are spent in dreaming.

The Nature of Dreams

Dreams are essentially hallucinatory experiences occurring in normal people while they are asleep; they closely resemble the experiences undergone by wakeful people in some abnormal mental state, which may be primarily due to physical causes as in toxic confusion or delirium, or to actual mental illnesses such as schizophrenia. Carl Jung wrote " Let the dreamer walk about and act like one awakened and we have the clinical picture of dementia praecox " (Schizophrenic psychosis).

The visual content of dreams are mostly recapitulations of actual things seen in daily life, perhaps often and recently, sometimes rarely and long ago; what we hear in dreams is also related to past perceptual experience. Occasionally we may act in dreams as well as being acted upon, and this activity may sometimes be apparent to other people, when we mutter, talk, or sit up and walk about: a sleep-walker is essentially a mobile dreamer.

While we dream we are almost completely out of touch with reality but some messages can reach us from the world outside or from our own body, and show that they have done so by being woven into the fabric of the dream: for instance, a full bladder may lead to dreams of swimming, rainfall or simply urination; a ringing bell may appear in a dream as church bells; the pressure of a fellow sleeper's arm thrown over neck or chest to dreams of hanging or suffocation. So, dream experiences are partly influenced by the sleeper's limited and selective perception of real stimuli.

The length of the dream is usually proportional, in the wakened dreamer's estimate, to the actual physiological dream time when this is assessed by observation of eye movements and electro-encephalographic studies; but it still remains likely that some dreams which seem extremely long to the subject last in fact only a few seconds.

Dreams are difficult to describe, for a variety of reasons. Firstly, they are often bizarre and complex, full of subtle interweaving images, sometimes resembling Chinese boxes in their construction, and rich with humour and pathos, even occasionally transcendental. We sometimes cannot find words adequate to express the rich nature of our dreams, and when we relate them are surprised and disappointed at their apparent banality and the listener's obvious boredom.

Secondly, they are forgotten with a rapidity that seems doubly surprising in view of the tremendous air of importance and significance, and the sharpness of focus that they possessed during their actual occurrence. This failure to memorise dream material or actually to learn from it is partly explained by our desire to forget dreams which frightened or shocked us; there are many dreams that one cannot recall without shame or disgust. But it hard to understand why an amusing dream on recall seems so much less funny, if indeed it can be remembered at all.

In waking life we sometimes meet with a situation that seems strangely familiar to us although we are sure that we can never have encountered it before—the phenomenon of *déjà vu*. It is not unlikely that the new real experience has mobilised from our memory store a similar or identical dream experience that has become inaccessible to us through the dynamism of repression.

Theories About the Nature and Function of Dreams

The Dream as a Supernatural Experience

In cultures where sleep is thought to be transient death or migration of the soul, dreams are usually regarded as " possession " of the dreamer's mind by supernatural agencies, divine or demoniacal. In such cultures dreams are often regarded as literally or symbolically prophetic, an attitude by no means dead in European minds. Clearly where these beliefs are firmly held, dreams may in fact influence actions or the interpretation of events; they have a real function as a source of guidance for the believer.

The Dream as a Perceptual Disorder Accompanying Sleep

Dreams can be simply dismissed as hallucinatory disturbances of normal sleep when one individual compensates for the lack of real perceptions by supplying visual, auditory and other images from the enormous storehouse of his memory. Similarly, they can be regarded as elaborate misinterpretations of actual stimuli reaching the sleeper's sense organs. There is no doubt that such phenomena do occur; dreams of swimming associated with a full bladder, or falling, when the sleeper actually falls out of bed, are common examples, but to accept this as the sole explanation of dreaming would imply a fantastically rich and complex response for every individual to the very limited number and variety of stimuli normally experienced by a man asleep.

The Dream as a Manifestation of Mainly Unconscious Mental Activity

Attempts to explain away dream life along neuro-physiological lines seem naïve and unconvincing. Dreams seem, and indeed are, more important to us than we may care to admit: they arouse feelings in the dreamer which are as intense and real as the emotions he experiences in the face of real happenings: a bad dream may leave him shaken and disturbed for many hours; and guilt can be as surely awakened by a dream action as it may be by an actual misdemeanour during waking life. The dreamer feels responsible for what he has dreamt, ponders over it, and seeks a meaning in it, even if he is a normal healthy adult with no personal or cultural tendencies to superstition or undue gullibility. It is a common experience that past and present anxiety, wishes and fears, are reflected in dreams, sometimes obviously, sometimes in a way instantly discernible by the dreamer or someone close to him, but not perhaps apparent to everyone. The dream is coloured by the personality, mood and experiences of the dreamer, and might be regarded as an extension of his mental life into those sleeping hours when his full consciousness can no longer select and arrange what images he shall dwell upon or what feelings these images may evoke. Wishes and dreads normally well hidden are revealed in dreams, and ruthlessly followed to their conclusion.

Why should our dreams so often contain images and actions which our waking selves would repudiate? Why, in spite of this content of bizarre and often repulsive material, do they seem so real? Why do dream events follow a logical sequence so that we can recognise cause and effect with certainty, even though these may be entirely incongruous when we recall them in the daytime? No simple theory of perceptual fill-in, or overspill or persistence of waking thought is adequate to explain these facts; they can only be understood in the light of the hypotheses evolved by the great pioneers of depth psychology —Sigmund Freud (1856–1939) and Carl Jung (1875–1961), respectively the founders of those schools of psychology known as Psychoanalysis and Analytical Psychology. Both men demonstrated that much of our conscious behaviour, which seems so rational and is so acceptable in daily life, is nevertheless influenced profoundly by wishes and fears rarely admitted into our waking conscious minds. These drives towards actions and inhibition against action may be inherent or acquired; what is certain is that dynamisms exist in the mind to keep hidden away at an unconscious level aspects of our own nature that would appal our adult, balanced selves. This form of personal censorship is aptly called " repression " (see Chapter 8). Both Freud and Jung also claimed that in sleep the censoring dynamisms falter and allow primitive, selfish and intolerable ideas and feelings to enter consciousness in the form of dreams. Jung went so far as to suggest that the dreamer might also admit from his unconscious mind creative drives, even racial memories of the momentous experiences of our forbears. Freud's great book *The Interpretation of Dreams* is an enduring monument to his powers of observation and speculation; in this great work he suggested that dreams become fully susceptible to analysis and explanation once we accept the proposition that an elaborate system of camouflage exists to convert the raw drives of our unconscious mental life into strange, ludicrous, but usually tolerable dream images. What we experience as a dream he termed the " manifest dream content " and this, he asserted, was the result of the " dream work " that process of repression and amelioration already referred to. The " latent dream content " was not in Freud's view a thing distinct from ordinary mental life, but simply the whole area of subconscious thought, always present when we wake or sleep but nearly always impossible actively to recall. Many different mental dynamisms are simultaneously involved in the "dream work"; these include the alteration of one idea into another, more bearable idea, that represents it with some consistency—"symbolisation"; the attribution of guilty and wicked wishes to other people—"projection"; and the transference of intolerable emotions from more to less painful areas of experience—"displacement". (Mental dynamisms are discussed more fully in Chapter 8.) That the "dream work" is not always adequate is clear from the disturbance apparently innocuous dreams may still generate in the sleeper, either while he sleeps or after he wakes. That it represents mental activity of a pace and type we can hardly reconcile with the idea of rest is aptly illustrated by any single dream, when it is remembered that the rapid succession of fantastic images not only exists in itself but is the product of "dream work" aimed at disguising and excluding other images. Freud considered that the ultimate purpose of the "dream work" is to protect sleep; to allow sleep to continue. Certainly when it fails, terrifying, oppressive ideas enter the dream, the sleeper generally wakes, and may even be unable or very unwilling to sleep again. All of us have had nightmares, and our look of exhausted suffering when we wake accounts for the age-old attributes of bad dreams to the experience of being ridden over by a mare-headed goddess.

Once it is accepted that dream experiences represent the "royal road to the unconscious" one can readily understand why dreams are so soon forgotten; daytime repression is effective in hiding completely the half admitted horrors of the night.* Psycho-analytic techniques utilise the fine-drawn nature of this barrier between the conscious and unconscious minds to lay bare hidden motivations and feelings. Until quite recent years, psycho-analysts devoted a great deal of time to the study of their patients' dreams for the double purpose of diagnosis and treatment, and Jungian psychotherapists remain devoted to these methods.

---

* This theory should be compared to the suggestion made in Chapter 4 that dreams are not remembered because the sleepy brain cannot consolidate its memories.

SELECTED BIBLIOGRAPHY

1. *Sleeping and Waking.* Oswald, I. 1962. New York: Elsevier.
   A compendium of recent neurophysiological and psychological studies of alertness, drowsing, sleeping and dreaming. The E.E.G. changes characteristic of the states are well described and illustrated.
2. *The Interpretation of Dreams.* Freud, S. (trans. James Strachey). 1956. New York: Basic Books Inc.
   This is a recent translation of a classic study of dreams first published in 1900.
3. *An Introduction to Jung's Psychology.* Fordham, F. 1961. London: Pelican.
   Jung's writings about dreams are complicated and dispersed over many books and papers. Chapter VI contains an authoritative summary of his main theories on the subject of dream interpretation.

Chapter 14

THE EXPERIENCE OF PAIN

Pain as a Biological Process

Pain is an extremely broad term covering a variety of sensations experienced by all animals in response to certain stimuli. The sensations are nearly always unpleasant, and the stimuli nearly always dangerous to life or at least damaging to tissues. It is convenient to regard pain primarily as a protective mechanism, tending to make the animal not only aware of its discomfort but compelling it to lessen the discomfort by flight from the source of pain, or by immobility to reduce pain if it originates within the animal's own body. " Flight " can be local, as in the case of the simple spinal reflex arc that leads to withdrawal of a pricked or pinched limb; or general, as when the whole animal withdraws from a powerful noxious stimulus such as fire. Immobility, which has the effect of resting the skeletal system and decreasing peripheral demands on the heart and lungs, may be a useful response to severe, short-lived pain, especially when this arises in internal organs; it is often the response also to milder pain of long duration and may then represent an effort to lessen accompanying exhaustion, or to avoid the sharp exacerbations experience teaches the sufferer to expect as the result of activity.

Life *without* pain presents some grave problems. Rare cases are known of men and women who are born with little or no ability to perceive pain (congenital universal indifference to pain). These unfortunate people can sustain severe injuries without realising that their lives are endangered; they bruise, burn and cut themselves, may fracture a limb, or neglect to attend to minor injuries so that these become infected, all because they feel no pain. Such people display all the signs and symptoms of shock—pallor, fall in blood pressure, nausea, vomiting, sweating and thirst—when they suffer major injury although they feel no local discomfort: in physiological terms, they show normal segmental " withdrawal " and autonomic responses to noxious stimuli, these being mediated at spinal cord and brain stem level, but there is presumably some defect in the afferent pathways subserving pain perception at higher levels in their central nervous system.

Not to be able to feel pain constitutes a major disability; but it should not be assumed that pain is consistently useful either to the individual or the species. It may lead to such restlessness and exhaustion that appetite fails and healing cannot proceed; to depression, with its attendant risk of suicide in human beings; to ineffectual and sometimes damaging attempts to assuage local discomfort by scratching, pricking or rubbing the affected part, as anyone who has looked after a sick pet will have observed—though human beings, especially children and old people also tend to increase their own suffering in this way; and finally human pain of severe or protracted character calls for the administration of analgesic drugs, nearly all of which have some toxic side effects, whilst the most powerful are frequently drugs of addiction. There is also increasing evidence that the reduction in body movement that accompanies some types of pain can itself be harmful in certain circumstances; resting leads to a decrease in the local blood supply and nutrition, to tenderness and atrophic changes in the skin, wasting of muscles and inadequate absorption of exudates which may become organised into fibrous adhesions (within joint capsules, for example), thus producing a further limitation of power and movement. This vicious circle of pain; decreased movement—further damage—extended loss of power and mobility; is well known to athletes and dancers who are especially prone to mechanical injuries of their musculo-skeletal system: modern practice in physical medicine is to emphasise the importance of early mobilisation of injured joints and muscles even where movement exacerbates pain.

Finally, there are many conditions which threaten function, and even life itself, in which pain is either absent or appears as a late symptom when all hope of recovery from the pathological lesion is past.

Pain is, on all these counts, defective as a means of protection; in some cases it might be compared to a fire sprinkler which is set off far too late and may continue to dowse valuable goods long after the fire is out. A sounder basis for the study of pain than the teleological one usually advanced might be to regard it as possessing no function in its own right, but as being capable of initiating some useful responses, commonly termed " adaptive ", and some useless or downright deleterious ones, which we may call " maladaptive ".

Characteristic Features of Pain

Pain compels attention as can no other sensation. In states of wild excitement, or intense physical activity it may be unnoticed—soldiers on the battlefield sometimes experience grave injury without being aware of their state: preoccupation with other matters can keep the consciousness of pain in the background of the sufferer's mind, and simple distraction often lessens pain as every good nurse and most mothers know. All the same, severe pain may eclipse everything else in the world while it lasts, and no other common sensation makes so lasting an impression or so profoundly influences human conduct. The fear of pain, and pain itself, have for centuries been used in the service of authority, and this fear has even been extended beyond life, so that a physical hell of everlasting torment might be invoked to ensure good behaviour this side of death. Considering the primary significance of pain in human experience, its vocabulary is surprisingly restricted, and any classification based on simple descriptive terms tends to become subjective to the point of being scientifically useless. However, it is possible to make some broad generalisations about the nature of pain which are of practical importance to every doctor.

Varieties of Pain Perception

A patient may describe his pain to his doctor as " burning, crushing, tearing, piercing or stabbing ". In each case he is using past experience real or imagined, to try to convey his sensations. Many a surgeon has raised a dutiful laugh from his students by asking a patient how familiar he is with the effects of being stabbed, but surgeon, students and patients alike are all equally at a loss for any better way of describing a wholly subjective experience. Children, mentally defective people and men and women whose power to express themselves in words is limited are especially at a disadvantage in this situation. We are on safe ground when we attempt to isolate certain features such as location, mode of onset, duration and intensity.

Location

Generally speaking, sharp, smarting, burning or cutting pain characterises superficial lesions. Diseases of muscle, bones and joints often produce a dull, agonising, throb which the patient himself feels as " deep-seated ". Distension of hollow viscera often produces " colicky " pain which is often related to the appropriate area, but this picture is confused by the phenomenon of *referred* pain, in which sharp superficial discomfort is felt in the skin area subserved by the same sensory nerve roots that supply the diseased viscus.

Mode of Onset

Pain may start as a dull discomfort becoming gradually more intense, or begin at full severity, in which case accompanying shock is likely also to be severe.

Duration

Most pain varies in intensity from time to time during the day, even without distraction or treatment: constant unremitting pain is complained of sometimes in non-organic conditions. Pain can be fleeting but intense, or mild and long lasting.

Exacerbation

Pain of organic origin undergoes exacerbation in ways that are often highly characteristic—as in the sudden acute pain that wakens a sleeper with arthritis when the guarding muscles relax, or the increase in discomfort with postural changes in patients with infected lesions where variations in blood supply increase and decrease the local tension.

Intensity

Patients are even more at a loss when asked to assess the intensity of their pain than when describing its nature. An objective estimate can sometimes be made from the concomitant shock in acute conditions, or exhaustion, pallor and loss of weight where pain has been protracted. It is important to remember that a tearful and voluble patient may be suffering as much as a reserved and stoical one; habits of exaggeration and the use of dramatic descriptive terms do not automatically confer immunity from serious illness and pain on a patient.

Even allowing for wide individual differences in powers of expression and idiosyncratic response, pain is *not* proportional to the extent or severity of injury, but the number of free nerve endings involved. Brain tissue (apart from the meninges and blood vessels) is not provided with pain receptors and massive disease of the brain can occur without any discomfort; on the other hand a gentle touch on the corneal epithelium (which is particularly richly supplied with pain receptors) can produce exquisite pain.

Modification of Pain

It is generally held that adaptation to pain does not take place. All other sensory receptors become fatigued by continued stimulation, but pain sensation does not diminish simply by virtue of prolonging the application of a noxious stimulus. This said, it is an observed fact that the ability of animals to tolerate pain does vary from one individual to another and from time to time. Factors modifying the tolerance of pain can be classified as follows:

Individual Differences

Women are usually thought to tolerate pain better than men; extravert personalities on the other hand tolerate pain poorly, or at least respond to their suffering in a more vehement way. Small children have very low tolerance, but parental example and maturation generally combine to make them bear with minor aches and pains quite sensibly by the age of about ten.

Cultural Differences

The Spartans and North American Indians are historically remarkable as having achieved a quite extraordinary acceptance of discomfort by the use of social sanctions and training. The "stiff upper lip" school of behaviour in our own or at least recent times also places a very high value on stoical acceptance of suffering.

Distraction

Tolerance may be increased when attention is drawn away from pain by presenting alternative stimuli. These may be pleasant in themselves, as when music or a change of scene are used for this purpose, or simply very intense, as when " white noise " is employed during dental manipulations. This method of raising the threshold of pain perception was notably demonstrated in Pavlov's dogs who could be taught to accept intense faradic stimulation with equanimity if they were simultaneously or promptly rewarded with food. (This method of conditioning can result in the animal's showing signs of positive pleasure at receiving noxious stimulation.)

A special form of distraction is seen in " counter-irritation ", when one kind of pain is rendered more tolerable by the deliberate infliction of another. Usually massive superficial stimulation is used for this purpose, such as rubbing, pinching, scratching, heating or chilling the skin, and rheumatic patients in particular seem to find this diversion of attention from deep pain to surface pain especially helpful.

Chronicity

Pain that goes on for weeks or months may create its own tolerance. Chronically sick people endure discomfort which most of us would find hard to bear; they are still aware of their pain but have learnt to fit their lives to its demands, avoiding exacerbating circumstances and discovering which postures and activities most help them. On the other hand, severe prolonged pain with loss of sleep may result in diminished tolerance and lead to collapse.

Suggestion and Hypnosis

Simple kindness makes pain more bearable. Some people are easily influenced by suggestions made to them by those they respect and will be able to bear more if they are praised for their endurance, or less if they are fussed over and made to feel childishly dependant. A step beyond suggestion is the medical use of hypnosis to lessen both pain itself and the tension that arises from it. This is dealt with in Chapter 15.

The Administration of Drugs

The use of drugs to reduce the intensity of pain is widespread and has been practised for centuries. Mild analgesics like aspirin lessen pain, while more powerful ones, such as the opium alkaloids, abolish the sensation altogether. Hypnotic drugs usually do not reduce pain unless used in doses which produce unconsciousness—they are then called " anaesthetics " and not " analgesics ".

Some people derive benefit from taking inert substances under the impression that these are pharmacologically active, the so-called " placebo reaction ". These "positive placebo reactors" tend also to find relief from pain when given substances which are inactive, or active substances in doses normally inadequate for the purpose. This phenomenon is described fully in Chapter 18.

Pain as a Source of Pleasure

Pain is not always avoided or regarded as a necessary evil. We have already seen in the phenomenon of counter-irritation that one type of pain may be involved to diminish another, and this sort of reaction sometimes goes a step further so that the " chosen " pain is actually welcomed and felt as a pleasure. Again, the secondary effects of pain in promoting interest and sympathy may make the pain itself valuable to the sufferer. Aged, lonely and neglected people and some sufferers from mental illness may prize the opportunities for contact their pain brings them, and are often unwilling to be relieved of those symptoms which are the only important experience in their daily lives. They may actually seek help and treatment from a doctor but are most unlikely to find relief, let alone cure. Pain is an old friend to them, and the loss of pain would deprive them of their only claim to status and attention.

Sado-Masochism

To some people pain may be a pleasurable experience and one to be deliberately sought: at certain times and in certain circumstances they may inflict pain on themselves or induce others to treat them with cruelty. The erotic novels of the Marquis de Sade (1740–1814) explored the full range of torture both physical and mental in the service of sexual excitement and the term "sadism" is to-day applied to the deliberate infliction of pain and humiliation in non-sexual as well as sexual situations. Leopold von Sacher-Masoch (1836–1895) was also a novelist: his young heroes were constantly maltreated in the service of their imperious mistresses, and their creator has also been immortalised by having his name applied to the search for heightened sexual pleasure through suffering cruel treatment (masochism). Masochism is now used to cover all those attitudes and activities characterised by a desire for degradation and punishment.

Sado-masochism is probably an integral part of ordinary motivation in normal people. A delight in blood sports, boxing, wrestling, or indeed any activity that offers the spectacle of danger and suffering, is widespread. How can we explain this delight in giving and receiving pain, let alone reconcile it with the repugnance in which pain is held in the context of disease? Probably many factors operate together, some being innate and others learned. Studies of animals indicate how close is the relationship between displays of aggressive and submissive behaviour in mating patterns: in " normal " human sexual activity there are aggressive and submissive components well recognised in such terms as " pursuit by the male ", " enslavement ", and even " all's fair in love and war ". The law recognises that " not unwelcome force " is something quite different from criminal rape. Sexual excitement is often intensified by powerful sensory stimulation of non-sexual parts of the body. Pretended or actual infliction of mild pain at the height of sexual excitement is common, or sexual partners may share fantasies of sado-masochistic experience. Finally, the guilty anxiety that attends sexual acts in our society—perhaps augmented by faulty sexual education in many individuals—may be assuaged when love-making is actually or symbolically expiated through association with pain as punishment or some form of humiliation that may be regarded as mental pain. Outside specifically sexual experience, sado-masochism may well have a basic connection with the frequently observed urge in some human personalities to dominate and in others to accept domination.

Central Pain

After great and long continued pain, healing of the underlying lesion may not relieve the pain as it might reasonably be expected to do: some part of the body including its pain receptors, may even be removed by surgical excision, but the patient still claims that he is in pain and shows every objective sign that he is speaking the truth. Severe injuries to the limbs, particularly those involving major blood vessels and nerves are particularly liable to be followed by this phenomenon of " phantom pain " or " causalgia ".

The mechanism responsible is not fully understood. It seems quite likely that in some sufferers from causalgia their experience of pain has been so great and prolonged that it has been " learned " as part of their body sensory scheme, in other words, their " body image " now includes an area of intractable pain. This should not surprise us; after all, many patients who have lost parts of their body continue to feel that they are still intact; when a limb has been amputated they retain the idea of a limb in their body scheme, the so-called "phantom limb"; and it takes a long time for this perceptual experience to disappear. As might be expected, phantom limb and phantom pain often occur together.

Pain experience can then exist " centrally ", although it has been initiated by past peripheral stimulation. Pain that is felt in the mind occurs in many psychological illnesses, and is as real and disabling as peripheral pain; patients show all the exhaustion associated with intense physical suffering. Relief of the causal psychological disorder will usually alleviate or abolish the pain; but the mechanisms of such psychogenic pain are still obscure, and may be diverse.

The Pre-Frontal Cerebral Cortex and Response to Pain

In the 1930s Egas Moniz, Professor of Neurology in the University of Lisbon, noted the effects of ablating the frontal lobes of animals anterior to the motor cortex. Such animals not only thrived after the operation but became very docile and free from tension in the face of situations which previously terrified or enraged them: they also showed little or no reaction to noxious stimuli. For example, a cat so treated would continue to purr and eat while receiving powerful faradic shocks. He might move away from the electrodes, but would remain composed and good tempered. These brain-damaged animals in fact experienced pain, but the perception did not initiate emotional reactions or gross changes in behaviour, nor provoke any autonomic changes.

By 1936, at Professor Moniz's suggestion, this operation had been performed on sick human beings for the relief of otherwise intractable suffering. It was found that complete removal of the prefrontal areas was not essential; any interruption of the connections between the anterior and orbital surface of the prefrontal cortex and the dorso-medial nucleus of the thalamus would suffice, and simple division of the thalamo-prefrontal projection system has been found to lead to retrograde degeneration and death of ganglion cells in the dorso-medial thalamic nucleus. Such bilaterally " leucotomised " patients still experience pain but the perception is reduced in importance, their attention can be given to other things and, as one such patient put it: " Oh, I still have the pain but it doesn't bother me any longer."

The improvement in sleep, appetite, digestion and skin texture that accompanies this demotion of pain as the foremost sensation, suggests that the autonomic nervous system has been freed from subservience to signals triggered off by afferent pain impulses. The prefrontal cortex, the dorsomedial thalamic nuclei and the hypothalamus may be assumed in the intact animal to form an integrated functional system for—among other things—determining the response of the animal to pain perception.

Bilateral prefrontal leucotomy is a drastic procedure; it not only alters the way a patient reacts to pain but has many unwanted side effects, including loss of self-control and a coarsening and flattening of personality and emotional response. It seems possible that the capacity to respond to one's own pain with proportionate distress goes hand in hand with judgment and insight, and with an ability to imagine the feelings and sufferings of other people, and hence to that limitation of our primitive selfish behaviour which we term self-control; that internal discipline which is essential for the preservation of social life among such potentially dangerous animals as homo sapiens.

SELECTED BIBLIOGRAPHY

1. *Pain.* White, J. C., and Sweet, W. H. 1955. Springfield, Illinois: Thomas.
   A beautifully produced book, ranging over the anatomy, physiology, and psychology of pain mechanisms, and including the clinical applications of our present knowledge.
2. *Congenital Insensitivity to Pain: A Critique.* Sternbach, R. A. Psychological Bulletin, 1963. 60, 3.
   An intriguing review of the significance and effects of diminished or absent ability to feel pain.
3. *Pre-Frontal Leucotomy.* Partridge, M. 1950. Oxford: Blackwell.
   The first part of this book gives a useful summary of the neuro-physiological rationale and history of this drastic operation.
4. *Man Into Wolf.* Eisler, R. 1950. London: Spring Books.
   A scholarly study along anthropological and Jungian lines of man's irrational desire to inflict or suffer pain and humiliation.

Chapter 15

HYPNOTIC STATES

Hypnosis (from the Greek " hupnos "—sleep) is a condition super-ficially resembling natural sleep but differing from it in some important ways. The basic characteristic of the hypnotic state is an alteration in the behaviour of the subject so that he becomes intensely susceptible to suggestion: electro-encephalographic activity shows that he is either fully alert or at the most lightly drowsing; the plantar responses remain flexor and the pupils are not constricted.   The generally accepted picture of how a hypnotised person should behave varies from place to place, and such a person will usually conform to his own, and his culture's, expectations.   Thus the ordinary 20th-century European subject models his behaviour during hypnosis on an imita-tion of sleep (the " trance ") or sleep-walking; but in other parts of the world wild physical and mental excitement can accompany those phenomena we know to belong to the hypnotic state.   Amongst these manifestations may be listed some ritual dances common throughout Africa and Asia, and such religious cults as voodoo and snake-handling seem to employ hypnotic frenzy.

Susceptibility to Hypnosis and Individual Differences

Although it is sometimes possible to hypnotise oneself, the successful induction of hypnosis usually depends upon the establishment of a trusting relationship between subject and hypnotist: it is difficult or impossible to induce in people who are too young, too ill, too anxious or suspicious to co-operate.   Contrary to popular belief, emotionally unstable and exhibitionistic people are not usually easy subjects for hypnosis: public displays of hypnotism for entertainment were allowed in the United Kingdom until the passing of the Hypnotism Act (1952) and were often followed by protracted states of abnormal behaviour in some subjects long after the performance had ended.   It is likely that these vulnerable people were never in fact hypnotised at all (or indeed hypnotisable) and that they merely made use of a public occasion and mob excitement to behave in a way that attracted a great deal of attention to themselves.   In serious experimental work on hypnosis, the best subjects prove to be intelligent and co-operative men and women with well-developed powers of concentration.   Pregnant women and people who have freshly experienced great physical or mental suffering are usually excellent subjects, but this special aptitude is often transient.

It is possible to select people for their ability to achieve the hypnotic state by testing their capacity to concentrate on a fraction of the total perceptual field and to accept suggestions for changes in muscular power and posture. Three tests are commonly employed:

Hand-clasping. The subject is asked to clasp his hands together and to maintain a vice-like grip, he is then told his hands are locked together and he cannot release them easily.

Arm-levitation. He attempts with closed eyes to hold his arms out horizontally before him, while it is suggested to him that one or both arms are rising or falling.

Body-sway. He stands to attention, again with closed eyes, and is told that after a few moments he will begin to sway to and fro: a potentially good subject will shortly lose his balance.

Induction of Hypnotic States

The basic requirements for successful induction of hypnosis is the fixation of the subject's attention on a restricted part of the environment, usually selected by the hypnotist, who ensures a minimum of distraction by being if possible alone with the subject in a quiet place and asking him to lie down as if he were going to sleep. Indeed, the hypnotist may tell the subject that he is falling asleep while he listens to the hypnotist's even tone, or fixes his gaze intently on a single visual object—perhaps the point of a pencil; or he may be asked to concentrate on keeping a limb raised against gravity while the hypnotist suggests extreme tiredness, and complete relaxation of every other part of his body.

Bodily Changes with Induction of Hypnosis

The subject's muscles undergo profound relaxation, he sweats, his breathing alters in rate and depth, and he looks as if he is asleep. It is common for apparently spontaneous twitching, trembling, sighing and jerking to occur (" hypnotic autokinesis ") but these movements disappear as the trance becomes deeper. The subject remains alert to the hypnotist's voice and to any other stimulus suggested by the hypnotist, who actually now controls the subject's perceptual field. When this state is reached a variety of interesting phenomena can be observed.

Sensory Changes

Areas of the skin and mucous membranes can be made anaesthetic at the hypnotist's suggestion, or he may induce increased tactile and pain sensitivity in such areas (hyperaesthesia) or abnormal sensations (paraesthesia). The subject may be made to experience heat or cold and his reported experience may be accompanied by objective changes in the blood supply to the skin (see Autonomic Changes, below).

Changes in Voluntary Muscle Tone and Movement

Separate limbs, or the entire body may be made as rigid as a board (" hypnotic catatonia ") at the hypnotist's suggestion, limbs may be elevated or dropped, eyes may be opened or closed, speech may be elicited and the subject may be told to stand up, walk or perform a wide range of normally voluntary movements (" hypnotic somnambulism ").

Psychological Changes

Emotional changes ranging from black depression to frenzied gaiety (accompanied by their usual physical manifestations of weeping or laughter) can be suggested. Lost memories can be recovered, sometimes from infancy; some of these are verifiable with the waking subject, but some are undoubtedly fantasies. The hypnotist may suggest to the subject that childhood experiences are being relived and his general behaviour may then regress to the appropriate age level as long as the suggestion remains in force. Conversely, certain specified events may be forgotten at the hypnotist's suggestion.

It is also possible to suggest quite elaborate patterns of behaviour which the subject will follow out when hypnosis comes to an end. This is the well-known phenomenon of " post-hypnotic suggestion ". The subject may be told that exactly two minutes after emerging from his trance he will feel compelled to get up, go to the light switch and turn the room lights on and off eight times, returning to his seat with no memory of having ever been ordered to behave in this way. It seems probable that while his " automatic " action is in progress the subject has in fact reverted to a light hypnotic state which lifts when the action has been completed. Some post-hypnotic suggestions are obeyed reluctantly or partially, or may actually be resisted by the subject who will own to a strong (and to him quite irrational) desire to carry out the action that has been suggested. He may end by capitulation, and rationalise his compulsive behaviour: " I wanted to make sure that your light switches were working: I seem to remember your telling me they'd been giving trouble."

With very co-operative subjects it is not only possible to induce simple sensory changes such as have already been described, but even to persuade them to accept false beliefs (delusions) and misinterpretations of commonplace stimuli (illusions) or perceptual experiences divorced altogether from stimulation (hallucinations). These abnormal changes are fully described in Chapter 12: all that needs to be said here is that certain deeply hypnotised people can have their perceptual world most elaborately distorted by a hypnotist " feeding in " false perceptual data while carefully isolating his subject from the real world. One might fairly say that in deep hypnosis the subject has surrendered his perceptual system to his hypnotist. But it is doubtful whether this surrender is ever complete and unconditional; a hypnotic subject will not accept anything and everything suggested to him.

From these considerations emerge two questions of great medico-legal importance: can hypnotised persons be made to do things against their will? and, can one induce a subject to behave in hypnosis in a way that he would never do in ordinary life? The answer to both these questions is generally, no. It is usually impossible, or at least very difficult, to impose suggestions on a hypnotised person that run completely against the grain of his conscience, moral code and general style of life (though it must be remembered that any person may have unconscious or hidden motives for accepting suggestions that seem to be outside his ordinary range). Conversely, lengthy and intricate indoctrination, of the type we term " brain-washing ", would be necessary to induce a normally law-abiding and peaceful citizen to perform criminal acts, and it is probably significant that the condition in which " brain-washing " is feasible include intense physical and mental strain in the subject, sometimes with total isolation and great dread of possible death or torture for himself and his loved ones. In these circumstances it is clear that something more than, and perhaps different from, simple hypnotic suggestibility is at work.

It must not be assumed, however, that minor changes in attitude cannot be achieved by the use of hypnosis. Some specific states of unreasonable fear (" phobias ") can be ameliorated or abolished if the subject is reassured repeatedly while in the hypnotic state that the object of his dread—dogs, storms, feathers, open spaces or whatever it may be—is no longer able to alarm him.

Another question sometimes raised by the hopeful would-be subject is, whether skills may be acquired instantaneously or wonderful aptitudes revealed under hypnosis? Again the answer is no; but if anxiety is hindering the learning or performance of a skill, hypnosis may be used to lessen this anxiety and thus indirectly to improve function.

Autonomic and Semi-autonomic Changes

These can also be brought about during hypnosis. Changes in respiratory rate and depth, flushing due to cutaneous vasodilatation, and sweating have already been mentioned as common occurrences during the induction of hypnosis, and a fall in blood pressure and pulse rate often accompanies the relaxation produced by the " trance ". Should a state of physical or mental excitement be suggested to the subject, the respiratory and cardiac rates and the blood pressure all tend to rise: if he is told that a part of his body is hot, there may be observable cutaneous vasodilatation over that part, and he may even sweat excessively in the same area. An urgent desire to micturate, defaecate, yawn or cough may be induced, and salivation can sometimes be stimulated or inhibited. Surgical shock, which represents a reflex mass disturbance of autonomic function, is often conspicuous by its absence or mildness following operations conducted under hypnotic anaesthesia, and many obstetricians are convinced that pregnant women who have been trained in hypnosis before they go into labour, experience more efficient and far less painful uterine and abdominal contractions during the first and second stages; even if the hypnotist cannot be present during labour, post-hypnotic suggestions on his part for easy and powerful muscular contractions can be very effective.

Termination of Hypnosis

How does hypnosis end? Unless the hypnotist maintains influence over the subject's perceptions and keeps him relatively passive and dependent then the hypnotic state will spontaneously wane, and the subject will either wake, or pass into natural sleep. Whether or not on waking he recalls his experiences while under hypnosis will depend on whether suggestions for amnesia were given during the trance. Many skilled subjects wake feeling refreshed and alert, with clear memories of an experience enjoyed for its unique qualities of relaxation and peace.

Clinical Applications of Hypnosis

The clinical uses of hypnosis are still disappointingly few, partly because of the limited susceptibility of some individuals, and a tendency to increasing refractoriness in others, and partly because it makes heavy demands on the time of both doctor and patient. There is also, if we are to be honest, a disagreeable aura of charlatanism and the occult attached to the whole subject which makes many doctors as well as their patients reluctant to accept its use as an occasional valuable form of therapy. It is to be hoped that the banning of theatrical performances of hypnotism and the increased and better informed spread of psychological knowledge through newsprint and television will dispel some of the fears associated with the procedure in the public mind; while continuing scientific research with properly controlled experiments may help to make it more acceptable to the profession.

At present hypnotism is used, often in conjunction with suitable medical treatment, to assist in relaxing tense patients and to reduce the intensity of disabling fears. Also in the psychiatric field it can be used to recover lost memories of traumatic events which may be contributing towards neurotic states and to help some subjects release pent-up emotion.

The intractable itching of some skin diseases may be eased by frequent and patient hypnotherapy, as also may spasmodic bronchial asthma. Major and minor operations, notably dental treatment, can be successfully carried out under hypnosis, but modern drug-induced anaesthesia is so safe and effective that there are few indications for the hypnotic variety.

Perhaps the greatest field for hypnotherapy lies in midwifery, where training given during pregnancy can—as we have already described—lead on to a comfortable and effective experience of childbirth.

SELECTED BIBLIOGRAPHY

1. *Medical Hypnosis* (2 volumes). Wolberg, L. R. 1948. New York: Grune and Stratton.
   A complete and authoritative account of hypnotic methods and their application to psychotherapy. This work is a classic.
2. *Experimental Hypnosis.* le Cron, L. M. 1952. New York: Macmillan.
   This is an absorbing account of some modern scientifically conducted studies of hypnosis. All the contributions are of the greatest value.
3. *Battle for the Mind.* Sargant, W. 1957. London: Heinemann.
   The subject of " brain-washing ", briefly touched upon in the foregoing chapter, is fully discussed.

Chapter 16

THE DEVELOPMENT OF SKILLS IN THE FIRST THREE YEARS OF LIFE

Introduction

No other mammal is born so helpless as the human baby; puppies and kittens are blind at birth but can move along their mother's abdomen to find her teats; young monkeys can cling from birth to the mother's body even when she climbs and leaps in the treetops; young marsupials, though relatively far smaller may fairly be considered as continuing their intrauterine existence in the pouch—yet even they can make the journey from the external genital area to the safety of the pouch unaided. The human baby is born with the power to grasp strongly, but in the absence of long body hair on his mother this is of little use to him; he cannot move over a surface, or even turn himself from one side to the other. He can only locate the nipple by being taken up to his mother's breast and without her active care he could never survive.

By three years old the picture has radically changed. Puppy and kitten are full grown and sexually mature; such few useful habits as can be easily taught them are well established, but there is little chance of their learning anything new. Young monkeys and apes can learn more and continue to learn for longer; but they will not in the course of their whole lives achieve the social, communicative, reasoning and experimental abilities of the human child of three.

In these first three years all the basic physical skills are developed, and in addition the little human has advanced from a state of absolute egocentricity in which all behaviour is aimed at the immediate gratification of his own wishes to a condition where the demands of others in his immediate circle are at least recognised and sometimes respected. Millenia of social development in the species have been encompassed in an amazingly brief time, and yet this young child is still far from physical maturity and has a vast amount to learn. His continued capacity for learning alone would mark him out from all other animals, as would his often frantic and frustrated desire to learn. Other animals acquire those skills essential to preserve themselves and their species; domestic animals conditioned to wish to please their owners may learn irrelevant simple skills at their owner's whim; primates alone seek out new tasks and delight in mastering them and among primates the human child is pre-eminent in his wish to learn, to grow and to achieve adult status.

Basic to the development of human children is the recognition of the identity of his parent or parent-substitute. Lorenz has shown how brief a time is available for the young of other animals to learn the nature of their own mother; " imprinting ", as this phenomenon is called, must usually take place within the first few days, sometimes hours of life (see Chapter 4). It is probably significant that young humans can to some extent accept and identify as parent almost any adult who acts in a parental way towards them throughout their early years (a baby must be at least four to six months before he shows unmistakable ability to recognise and begin to prefer his own mother). This capacity to choose other persons to imitate and emulate remains with us all our lives and undoubtedly assists in our prolonged education.

How the Baby Develops

Children are not miniature adults. Their needs are different, and so are their skills although these differ in quality as well as extent. The child's power of reasoning is not only less than that of an adult but is different in kind. What seems a logical proposition to a bright three-year-old could be seen through by any adult. Even the brilliant child cannot skip the stages of normal psychological development, though he will probably achieve some skills earlier than his contemporaries.

We are indebted to many workers for studies of development. As early as 1787 Tiederman in Germany published a detailed account of one child's growth. Charles Darwin nearly a century ago (1877) reported the stages of development of one of his own ten children, describing the rooting reflex, hand co-ordination at six weeks, the display of anger at ten weeks and of laughter at three months. In 1930 Charlotte Bühler published a classic study *The First Year of Life*. From 1930 onward Arnold Gesell and his co-workers at the Yale Clinic of Child Development produced many detailed studies, including films, of very large numbers of children which established normal values for all sorts of skills and patterns of behaviour.

The development of skills is continuous. Casual observation suggests otherwise, but skills which appear " suddenly " have in fact been maturing during phases of apparent latency. Thus a child is said to take its first step on a particular day, but the preparatory " work " of achieving balance and co-ordination leading up to the first step takes place over many months. During illness or emotional distress recently acquired skills may disappear for a time; sometimes when these skills reappear they show actual advance on their former level. Again a child's delighted exploitation of a new skill may push other developing powers into temporary eclipse, and the untrained observer impressed by a two-year-old's dramatic growth of vocabulary may fail to notice how he is walking on a narrower base and with far fewer falls than six months before.

Development depends upon the maturation of the central nervous system, especially the myelination of nerve fibres. This process requires *time*, and though opportunity, training and encouragement are probably all helpful factors, maturation is dominant. Premature infants appear backwards by the usual standards for this reason, since their chronological age does not represent the actual time during which their central nervous system has been developing. Brain damage in the perinatal period also leads to varying degrees of developmental retardation since development also depends upon the anatomical and functional integrity of the C.N.S.

The direction of development of physical skills is cephalocaudal. At birth the baby's activity is dominated by the area including nose, lips and cheeks—he might be said to be " snout-centred ". His great skill is suckling, he possesses a rooting reflex, can swallow, cough, yawn, and sigh, sneeze and cry. Soon, the whole head becomes active with purposive and co-ordinate eye movements developing a little ahead of postural control of the head and neck. Later, hands begin to achieve their own powers, and later still the trunk can be raised and turned. The power to crawl, stand and walk follows the ability to sit unsupported and finally the sphincters of bladder and anus come under voluntary control. (Some of the most important innate response mechanisms shown by a newborn baby are described at the end of this chapter.)

Innate undifferentiated motor responses, massive and non-volitional, give way to specific localised co-ordination of movement. Automatic responses are replaced by purposeful activity. The Moro and tonic neck reflexes disappear after the first few weeks of life, as does the stepping reflex. The grasp reflex is lost by the end of the third month. Deliberate head and limb movements can now be attempted.

The rate of development is unique for the individual. The sequence of development is universal for normal members of the species. This is true for the simple basic skills, but does not hold good for those later acquired abilities which depend largely on opportunity and training. It is possible to establish norms for every skill but interpretation of individual variation requires much care and experience.

Racial differences have been noted, although cultural factors cannot be eliminated. Geber and Dean working in Uganda, demonstrated in 1957 that certain African children have more rapid *early* rates of development, and are apparently more mature at birth than European babies. For example, many newborn babies in Uganda displayed excellent head control and were able to drink from a cup.

Practical Value of Developmental Studies

Clinical Uses

Abnormal development can be distinguished from normal. For example, some lesions of the central nervous system can be detected in very early life, as can those developmental disorders due to inborn errors of metabolism. Some endocrine and biochemical disorders such as hypothyroidism, phenylketonuria, and galactosaemia, produce characteristically severe slowing of the developmental pattern. Psychological and mental disorders can also disturb the general pattern in various ways.

Psychometric Uses

Developmental maturity may be assessed from comparison of an individual's skills with the performance expected at his age. Fitness for adoption can be judged in this way; in physically handicapped children estimates can usefully be made of their maturity to decide on suitable forms of remedial treatment at a very early age. The response to treatment of children with metabolic disorders can be measured.

Prediction of Future Ability

There is a good deal of controversy about the prognostic value of development studies in the early years.

The estimation of future intelligence, skills and personality is not absolutely straightforward. In general, skills involving reasoning, learning or communication (i.e. the development of speech, concentration, alertness and perseverance, imitation, experimentation and richness of emotional response) have greater predictive value than locomotor or manipulative ability. Such estimates, however, can only be undertaken by experienced workers who keep constantly in mind the child's background and health, both past and present, as well as the quality of his actual test performance.

Some Important Patterns of Development

General Responsiveness

Mainly visual skills. At birth the baby sleeps or drowses most of the time, and responds with mass reflex movements to crude stimulation. By four weeks, he fixes his gaze on large objects confronting him. By twelve weeks, he turns his eyes in the direction of sounds. By sixteen weeks, he looks at his hands and at small objects nearby. He cannot reach with his hands but he " reaches with his eyes ". By six months, he changes his position to watch but cannot follow rapidly moving objects for another six months.

Mainly auditory skills. By three months, he turns his head towards a sound. By eight months, he responds to his name. By nine months, he imitates sounds. By one year, he understands the meaning of several words.

Mainly social skills. By six weeks, he smiles at the sound of his mother's voice, the sight of her face (or a simple mask without features). At two to three months, he vocalises with pleasure, wriggles in delight, and likes a mask to have features. At five to seven months, he can tell mother's face from others. He can show dislike of strangers, and plays with his mother and his toys. At seven months, he responds to the command " no ". He dislikes having his face washed. At one year, he obeys simple requests. He says three to four words, but understands many more. He loves rhythmic repetitive play. In the second year, his speech becomes more comprehensible; his vocabulary increases up to about 200 words. Short sentences are formed. In the third year, he begins to ask " why? " He becomes aware of himself as a person in a real world, and begins to dispute the authority of adults even when this is obviously benevolent. Rich fantasy play expresses his hopes and fears and *magical* ideas about causality. His vocabulary increases very greatly in this period.

Postural control. By twelve weeks, the head can be kept above the plane of the body when in ventral suspension. By twenty-four weeks, the child can sit up with support. By thirty-six weeks, he can sit unsupported. By forty weeks, he can pull himself up from the supine to a seated position. By about twenty months he will sit down adult fashion, buttocks first.

Locomotion. At thirty-six weeks he can support himself by holding on when standing. At forty weeks he can crawl on his belly, sometimes backwards, or he may " prefer " to roll, or shuffle on his bottom. By one year he lifts his abdomen off the floor and goes on all fours like a bear. He may move sideways like a crab, or " cruise " (the term for moving on his own feet while holding on to surrounding objects). By fifteen months, he can walk unsupported, unsteadily, with feet planted far apart (wide-based gait). He can crawl upstairs. Movements *with* gravity defeat him. He cannot get downstairs, nor lower himself gently from a standing position. By two years he can stoop without falling to pick up a ball, he can pick and throw, walk upstairs, and break into a run. By three years he can walk downstairs, one step at a time, and ride a tricycle, and hop on one leg.

Manipulation. At birth many babies can get their fingers to their lips, and thumb sucking is possible within a few days. By three months he attempts to touch and grasp but he cannot co-ordinate hand and eye so as to estimate distance and position. By five months, he picks objects up with both hands, can retain an object in his palm, and puts everything into his mouth. At about nine or ten months he can deliberately *grip* with his fingers, and can deliberately *release* objects by twelve months. By thirteen months he can put a small brick on top of another. He also begins to feed himself. At two he can turn over the pages of a book singly, tries to undress himself, scribbles with a pencil, unscrews lids and opens doors by turning handles. By three he attempts representational drawing and can build a tower of nine or ten bricks; he builds " laterally " now—bridges and trains.

Sphincter control. From birth or soon after, reflex voiding of bladder and sometimes bowels occurs after feeds and is used by some mothers as socially convenient. At about two years diurnal bladder control is established; nocturnal control usually follows before the fourth birthday. It is very unwise to attempt to assess development from a child's management of toilet habits. Social pressures and differences between mothers in their methods of dealing with " potting " make it impossible to be sure whether a child is truly backward or simply resistant to demands. Prolonged failure to establish acceptable habits is at least as likely to be due to emotional disturbance as to retarded development.

The Social Value of Slow and Prolonged Human Development

If young human beings were able to live as independent creatures and to procreate in their early years they would not have the time to acquire more than a fraction of the knowledge accumulated by their forbears, and mankind would then resemble the lower animals in having to learn by trial and—often fatal—error. Skills of communication would atrophy and family life would be disrupted by the emergence of powerful self-assertive drives in sexually mature persons without benefit of experience, especially that of others.

If female children could have babies themselves the time-consuming skills of child bearing and rearing would ensure their permanent subservience to mature aggressive males; we would have reverted to the primitive society represented by the primate hordes. The long-drawn-out immaturity of man to-day operates to his social advantage; the very helplessness of the human baby invites love and care, the baby learns to respond to love, to imitate those he loves, and only when he achieves full intellectual growth does he move on from dependence on parental care to the reciprocal relationship of courtship, marriage and family life.

FOOTNOTE

Some important innate response mechanisms have been noted as occurring in newborn babies. These are described as below.

1. *Moro Response.*

First described in 1918. A sudden very loud noise, or a major passive movement, will often produce a startle reaction characterised by crying, abduction and extension of the arms, extension of the head and trunk, and occasionally abduction and extension of the legs. Then the arms are adducted and flexed. A response that disappears in healthy babies by the age of two or three months.

2. *Rooting Response.*

Any light and localised touch on the " snout " area makes a baby move his head and open his mouth in search to pop the stimulus-source into his mouth. This is the basic mechanism that assists the baby to find the nipple by touch, not by sight.

3. *Tonic-neck Responses.*

Head position and tonicity of the neck muscles mainly determine the general posture of the neonate. The most characteristic tonic-neck response is the so-called " fencer's posture ", an example of an asymmetrical reaction: when a baby's head is (for example) turned to the right as he lies supine, his right arm and leg tend to be extended, and the left arm and leg flexed. Although this response clears after the age of two to three months, it may linger in the older drowsing infant who uses his flexed arm to stroke his hair while he turns his head and sucks the thumb or fist on the other side.

4. *Grasp Response.*

Pressing or stroking the palm results in a powerful and sustained grip, and tugging against the grip brings into play tensing of all the muscles of the arm. This response disappears in normal babies by about three months.

5. *Stepping Response.*

A neonate is held so that the soles of his feet touch a firm surface, this stimulus provokes a clumsy and automatic simulation of " walking ". The response disappears by the age of about a month.

SELECTED BIBLIOGRAPHY

1. *The First Five Years of Life.* Gesell et al. 1940. New York: Harper.
2. *The Development of the Infant and Young Child: Normal and Abnormal.* Illingworth, R. S. 1963. Edinburgh: Livingstone.
3. *The Abilities of Babies.* Griffith, R. 1954. London: University of London Press.
4. *The Developmental Progress of Infants and Young Children.* Sheridan, M. D. 1960. London: H.M.S.O.
   An inexpensive and useful resumé of the principal milestones of development.
5. *King Solomon's Ring.* Lorenz, K. 1957. London: Pan Books.

Chapter 17
CHILDHOOD

" Among the signs of . . . failure to reach emotional maturity are inability to think independently of ancestral and parental attitudes, even though these attitudes developed under conditions of survival quite different from those of the present time; feelings of guilt associated with changing of early inculcated attitudes or rules, superstitions . . . unreasoning fears, hates or hostility; hero-worship, and its use in avoiding social responsibility; exaggerated importance placed on such values as personal group power, prestige, ' face ', conformity in thinking, wealth, possessions . . . all these and many other distortions (of personality) contribute to the inability to use the whole personality for co-operation in common purposes for the enrichment of human life. . . ."

Dr. Brock Chisholm. (From a foreword to an annual report of The World Federation for Mental Health.)

The human animal leading a complex social life has more to learn than any other; he is born utterly helpless and dependent, but is expected in law by about twenty-one years to have become a fully grown reliable person accepting domestic and community responsibilities and exercising skills and judgments unattainable by any other animal. The processes by which he achieves these powers are as complicated and varied as the powers themselves, and the differences between any two human adults in physique and mental equipment are so great, even in homozygous " identical " twins, that we should not be surprised if we find it difficult to say what is the desirable endpoint of emotional development in the individual. The paragraph quoted at the start of this chapter emphasises what is *not* desirable and a close examination of Dr. Brock Chisholm's words shows that much of what he considers " immature " behaviour is behaviour which, far from being antisocial, represents too easy a capitulation to some unreasonable social pressures. The picture that emerges is one of " normal " adult human beings unable to assert themselves; to some extent, therefore, unable to set a fair value on themselves as separate members of the species, unable to make choices based on their own experience and observation, or to move forward from uncritical acceptance of what their group considers desirable at the moment, to what might suit a wider group at a distant time.

A more widespread, equally valid view of immaturity is that which equates it with criminal behaviour—the " mixed-up " kid of fiction can be almost any age in actual fact; the constant recognisable feature of his or her behaviour is an intense selfishness shown by an absolute inability to postpone or modify any strong personal wish, even if its gratification must damage others or infringe their rights. These people are not difficult to recognise when their activities bring them up against the strong displeasure of the community but many of them are intelligent enough to stop short of breaking the law, or even so clever that they can break the law and evade detection. Where Dr. Chisholm's immature individuals hardly seemed to realise their own identities, these " immature psychopaths " do not appreciate the claims that others might make on their forbearance, and indeed often seem to expect unlimited patience on the part of the community.

By combining these two views of immaturity we can perhaps arrive at a tentative definition of those qualities without which maturity cannot be reached.

A sense of personal identity, with a reasonable estimate of one's own powers and limitations.

A sympathetic appreciation of the claims and rights of others; this should include people right outside the family circle, social class, workmates, age group, even nation, since efforts to preserve the well-being of these groups are really hedonism extended, rather than true altruism.

The ability to balance these interests when they come into conflict, and to make effective choices and decisions with an eye to their long-term effects as well as their immediate results.

We may recognise in any community people whose honesty, reliability, generous and intelligent behaviour arouse almost everyone's approval, and many more who much of the time and in most everyday situations can be counted upon to act rationally and with goodwill. Such people often seem dreary bores to their children during their adolescent years when ideals of behaviour include much more individual liberty, and ambitions seem limitless and never impossible of attainment. The balance and health of a community must surely depend on the interplay of young, vigorous, flexible personalities with more stable, slightly disillusioned, necessarily more pessimistic ones: it is a sad moment in a man's life when he first realises that he has been granted no special immunity from failure, illness, bereavement, old age and death; yet he cannot be said to have reached full emotional growth until this time comes.

A word must be said of those people whose childish and irresponsible behaviour goes hand in hand with great creative or interpretative powers. Not every artist, writer, composer or entertainer (using the word in its widest sense) is emotionally immature, and many achieve the same stability as ordinary people. All discipline themselves to the needs of their gifts in a way no simply selfish person could ever manage. But there are many whose actual lives reveal destructive infantile tendencies, either self-directed and observed as carelessness of health and even life, as in the alcoholism of the dramatist O'Neill, and the drug addiction of the painter Modigliani; or outwardly turned, as when the poet Rimbaud outraged friends and enemies equally by his harsh and inconsistent conduct. For this reason alone we would do well to avoid using " moral " terms when discussing mature behaviour; it must be a very sick and stagnant community that cannot find room for a Shelley or a Baudelaire.

Again the immature, rebellious, self-destructive behaviour that characterised some (not, of course, all) members of the underground movements in Nazi-occupied Europe, must earn our constant gratitude. Solid conforming citizens with high respect for the community's standards can be induced to stand by and permit atrocities, even, alas, commit atrocities themselves, if the " mores " of their society sanction these evils. To find an acceptable definition of ideal mature behaviour we do better to go to a poet than a sociologist, and we have permission to quote *in extenso* from Laurie Lee's wishes for the future character of his newborn daughter, which demonstrate a wish for human beings to do more than merely to maintain the status quo.

". . . I'd ask her to preserve life both in herself and others. To prefer always societies for propagation and promotion rather than those for the abolition or prevention of.

Never to persecute others for the sins hidden in herself, nor to seek justice in terms of vengeance: to avoid like a plague all acts of mob-righteousness; to take cover whenever flags start flying: and to accept her frustrations and faults as her own personal burden, and not to blame them too often, if she can possibly help it, on young or old, whites or coloureds, East, West, Jews, Gentiles, television, Bingo, trades unions, the City, school milk, or the British Railways."

When we study the growing child and watch the unfolding of human personality we begin to appreciate the need for wise observation and imaginative loving care. We increase our own maturity when we can extend these attitudes to everyone who is unable for reasons of age, race, poverty or illness to occupy the privileged position of a doctor or medical student in the Western World to-day.

From Babyhood to Early Childhood— The Preschool Years

The behaviour of the baby under three months is characterised by complete egocentricity. His day is mostly spent in sleep, interrupted by phases of alertness during which he feeds, and is cleaned and cared for by his mother. These brief periods of handling and holding are of great importance; they mean an intense contact with one other person, permitting the satisfaction of some of his needs, which pleases him, and the denial of others which leads to his displaying infant rage—as, for instance, when he is taken from his warm cot and stripped for bathing.

By six weeks he shows his appreciation of the pleasure his mother's cuddling and kindness give him by smiling when she picks him up, and often by crying when she puts him down; but any adult who pays him attention, and even a mask roughly representing a human face, will elicit a smile. The three-month baby is everybody's friend, the typical laughing, lively cherub of advertisements and illustrations. At this stage he is beginning to play; he looks at a rattle with great longing and shakes it for a moment if it is placed in his hand. A few more weeks must pass before he can reach out and pick it up for himself, and thus begin to discern the separate nature of himself and his plaything. His mother's pride in his prowess interacts with his own zest in attempting new feats to extend the relationship between them and increase its reciprocity. By seven months he prefers her to every other adult; he will cry at the approach of a stranger, but cry bitterly at his mother's briefest absence. As soon as he can crawl he will follow her from room to room, and this " clinging " phase lasts well into his second year.

His love for his mother, for so it can now fairly be called, soon begins to include the wish to please her, to see her smile and to hear her friendly, approving voice: conversely he hates her to scold him, reacting with tears or protesting rage to an angry word. He laughs at her laughter, and sobers when she is depressed; but his need to be comfortable and happy at all times is still paramount, and he still demands instant gratification of his whims.

Feeding behaviour in the first year reveals much of the personality of mother and baby. The gentle unhurried handling of the young baby during his feeds leads to a stage when the satisfied suckling may actually relinquish his mother's nipple or the teat of the feeding bottle to smile up in her face. Weaning on to solid foods usually takes place in our society by about nine months. Present practice assumes that a choice of solid foods should be made available to babies weighing over fifteen pounds, and that ordinary family meals, a little simplified, will be taken by a year. The significance of weaning for the baby is very great. A meal is now no longer a close, shared experience between himself and his mother, in which his needs are all important, but a social occasion, with other members of the family claiming some of her attention, and perhaps helping her to attend to him. He extends his interest and goodwill to the family circle, though at times he will show his determination to dominate by noisy and messy behaviour and awkward likes and dislikes ("fads").

About this time he is learning to walk, and becomes increasingly adventurous. He learns that hard things hurt, but falls and bumps are soon forgotten as he sees something new to explore. A new and important social demand arises: he is required to pass urine and faeces into a special receptacle. At first he can see no point in this, and shuffles happily round the floor on his pot. Sooner or later he does what is expected of him and notices his mother's joy at his cleverness. She, not unnaturally, finds his recalcitrance over potting increasingly annoying as she realises that he can in fact control his bowel and bladder. This is a fruitful field for conflicts between mother and child, especially if neighbours and in-laws add their disapproval to her own displeasure.

From eight or nine months the baby begins to make distinct sounds, instead of simply cooing and gurgling. Soon he can name the adults around him and his own possessions. By two years he will possess a useful vocabulary and understand much more than he can say. His family is delighted by his speech and greets each new word with admiration: he loves the sound of his own voice, and begins to sing, sometimes songs of his own composition, sometimes simple nursery rhymes. He is beginning to achieve a more acceptable claim on adult attention than the helpless appeal of his babyhood, which he now rejects, or the loud contrariness of the child of one year, constantly "getting into things".

Throughout the two- to five-year-old period there is conflict between the drive for self-assertion on the toddler's part and his wish to conform, reinforced by the demands his family makes on him to "behave himself". So immature a personality cannot manage so intense a conflict, and at times the child's disturbance boils over in tantrums and other types of hostile, aggressive behaviour often directed at his mother. The whole period has been called "the Age of Spite", but this is to paint too black a picture. Often the toddler's desire to please can be clearly seen in his imitative behaviour at play, and in his earnest desire to help around the house or in the garden. It is better to think of this as a testing time when the young child tries to find out for himself the limits beyond which he cannot go with safety; safety being defined in this context as the enjoyment of steady affectionate care.

The three-year-old can ask questions, and does, endlessly. Sometimes his questioning is so persistent that his mother rightly interprets it as aggressive and tells him to be quiet and go away; but at other times his curiosity is genuine, his desire to understand what is going on around him both touching in itself, and highly important for his development.

Play is a subject in itself, for through play the young child achieves a mastery of his environment which his small size and lack of experience make impossible in his real life. Whether he is handling inert materials, such as sand and clay, or solid symbols such as dolls and toy trains, or playing with other children in games of shared fantasy, he is constantly practising and perfecting skills, from the simple manipulations involved in building a tower of bricks to the complex social skill of sustaining goodwill in a group for long enough to act out a fantasy or get to the end of a simple game with cards or dominoes.

By five years old the child in this country is considered to be ready for school: in other words he is assumed to be reasonably independent of his mother, able to dress and undress himself, to control his bowels and bladder, to sit still and attend for some minutes together, and to be able to mix with other children without too much aggression or timidity. All these abilities can break down under stress, and going to school for the first time is stress of a high order; but in general the five-year-old shows sufficient adaptability and confidence for the experience to be a welcome extension of his interests and abilities.

Factors Influencing Emotional Development in Early Childhood

There are so many factors modifying the changes that occur during the first five years of life that only the briefest mention can be made of them.

Individual Differences

No two children are absolutely similar and the same stage of development may be reached at very different times. Again some children tend towards dependence and passivity while others seem constitutionally rebellious from the earliest months.

Birth Order

Some workers, notably Alfred Adler, discern a clear relationship between birth order and personality. In his view first children tend to be pessimistic, cautious and conforming (perhaps because they are more dependent on adult approval than their younger siblings). Second children, who have to compete for attention, tend to be more aggressive and rebellious. The third (or youngest child) may accept the role of baby and always remain clinging and passive; or may resemble the second in his determination to excel.

Parental Handling

Emotional behaviour is profoundly modified by the parents' handling of the young child. Some mothers are endlessly patient and seem to invite aggressive behaviour; others are soon exhausted and meet every enquiry or effort to experiment on a toddler's part with a sharp word or a slap. Fathers are just as variable, some expecting far too much at every stage and others indulging the child's least whim in order to avoid disturbance of any kind. Most parents manage to steer a course between the extremes though all can be more tolerant at some times than at others. Ill-health, financial worries and bad housing are adverse factors, often making it very hard for parents to do their best for their young children.

Jealousy

This powerful emotion is experienced by every child on the arrival of the next baby, no matter how much thought the parents may have given to preparing him for the new arrival, or how well he may conceal his feelings (even from himself) in order to manage the welcoming behaviour that will win adult approval. Jealousy of the younger child may lead to open hostile behaviour towards mother and baby persisting for a variable time and often recurring in later childhood and adolescence, or to concealed hostility in the form of an unnatural solicitude. Children feel guilty and miserable when in the grip of jealousy, and show this by becoming silent and withdrawn.

Special Handicaps

Physical handicaps greatly effect emotional development, since they greatly diminish the independence possible for the child. Handicapped parents are also a great disadvantage. Children growing up with only one parent may be regarded as being under a special handicap; they cannot turn from one parent to the other at times of estrangement, and they may have to attempt precociously to fulfil the emotional needs of a bereaved adult.

Prolonged Separation from the Mother: Maternal Deprivation

We have repeatedly stressed the growing reciprocity of the child's relationship to his mother, and its implications for his healthy development. What happens if this relationship comes to an end temporarily, through separation by illness, or permanently through death? The effect will vary greatly with the age of the child and the availability of a substitute for the mother, and to some extent with the cause of the separation. Much attention has been focused in recent years on a common cause that can often be avoided—the hospitalisation of the young child. Let us follow the reactions of a hypothetical child of two years who enters hospital while quite fit for elective surgery—tonsillectomy or herniotomy, for instance. The following stages may be observed.

A phase of some *interest* in new surroundings, nurses, other children perhaps a new toy bought to help him " settle down ". This will last until the child's capacity to tolerate his mother's absence reaches its limit, when he will pass into a phase of *anxiety*. He looks round for his mother, calls her by name. When she does not appear, perplexity gives way to *rage*. He screams, hammers, shouts to express his anger at her failure to return. After a while he seems to realise the uselessness of his efforts, and *grief* follows, with bitter uncontrollable crying only abandoned when exhaustion sets in. After hours, or even days, of tears his loud misery gives way to *apathy*: he has lost hope. He sits or lies still, paying little attention to what is going on around him. Beneath his surface calm lies severe depression; an adverse experience of any kind, such as the loss of a toy, will result in renewed crying, but eventually even new disasters will hardly get his attention. He will submit quietly to injections, and has become a " model " patient. He goes back to an earlier type of behaviour (*regression*), displaying greater dependence and greater instability of mood and conduct than is normal for his age. If mother returns at this stage he is likely not to recognise her (*denial*); to her distress he will turn his head away, resist her caresses, even reject a proffered gift. Should he return home he will be extremely clinging (*insecurity*) demanding and sometimes making insatiable requests for sweets and toys, the concrete evidence of her continuing love. Many weeks will be necessary to re-establish his trust in her, for he has been, in his necessarily limited view, abandoned and betrayed.

This is not an exaggerated picture though it is a terrible one. Ten years ago nearly every hospital in this country admitted children in worse case than in our imaginary patient, some in pain and some terrified by delirium, and sent their mothers away with the assurance that " Your little boy will soon settle down. It's best to keep away; your visits will only make things worse." Indeed visiting was actually forbidden in many children's wards. Because hospital admissions of sick children, and admissions for later confinements of mothers of toddlers are among the common causes of separation, doctors bear a special responsibility to these categories of patients, and must always have in mind the long-term risk to emotional health of keeping mother and child apart. Daily visiting is a poor substitute for continuous care of a sick child by its own mother, but it is far better than allowing the child to believe itself utterly deserted in his time of need. We must point out here that there is some evidence that prolonged deprivation of maternal care—as with chronic illness or when the child is committed to an institution—may lead to intellectual impairment as well as emotional regression.

Children from Five to Twelve:
The Growth of Reasoning Ability

The main changes seen in children of this age are those associated with decreasing dependence on mother, family and home, and an increasing power to identify themselves with other children of the same age, at school or in the street. Children can spend all day at school by this time, and even manage visits to relations with pleasure, and in their daily play they very much prefer to do without an adult audience.

At five, children are usually absolutely certain about their own sex and are often curious about the bodies of other children. Playing at " hospital " or " school " is very popular and in mixed groups boys will be teachers or doctors (or fathers) and girls will be teachers or nurses (or mothers). By seven or eight most boys prefer playmates of their own sex: girls are more willing to mix, but will often be drawn to each other by male scorn.

Even in young children, mother's absence for any length of time may lead them to infer that she is dead, and in moments of rage they may even go so far as to wish for her death. By five or six the child has usually overheard sufficient adult conversation (and perhaps seen enough dead animals) to realise that death is an irreversible loss. He begins to formulate such practical ideas as " What would happen to me if mummy and daddy died? ", " Shall I die? ", and even " Wouldn't it be lovely if my little brother were dead?" These preoccupations frequently lead to behaviour greatly at variance with the cheerful confidence the child displays on other occasions; he may develop fears and dislikes (commonly of the dark, of animals, of going upstairs alone), start to suffer from nightmares, and to worry about improbable disasters. A seven-years-old starting off on a drive to the seaside may remark casually, " What will happen if the car crashes? " Intermittent tearfulness and sustained moods of depression occur in this age group, too, and suicidal thoughts are not uncommon. " I wish I could die ", may be one way of trying to imagine the relief of getting the thing over, so to speak; mothers may not realise that such feelings are very common in normal children, and that by ten years old, most children have come to terms with most of their fears: perhaps, in part at least, because they are now able to read, and this enlarging of their experience helps them to realise that even the loss of a beloved parent can be—and usually is—survived. (It is not simply a matter of chance that so many well-loved children's books begin with the ruthless killing-off of the hero's or heroine's parents.)

Before the onset of puberty the normal child will be able to do many arithmetical manipulations, write comprehensively in his own language and read most literary matter that is likely to come his way: his individual intellectual abilities, modified considerably by the quality of his home and school, will be bringing him into rich and varied contact with the experience of other people in other places and at different times in history. By twelve or thirteen he will think very much like an adult, much of the time. How has he achieved this ability?

Jean Piaget is the worker in this field to whom we owe most of our knowledge of the growth of reasoning ability. Professor Piaget (University of Paris and Geneva) has spent his life studying this problem and the following notes represent a tremendous (and sometimes arbitrary) simplification of some of his discoveries and conclusions. It must be remembered that these remarks apply to Western European children of the 20th century, that individual children vary greatly in basic intelligence, and that the simple " infantile " ways of thought mentioned as appropriate to very young children persist in adults and may never be fully replaced with logical, rational concepts.

From birth to one year a baby does not think. He is aware of sensations and can react with expressive behaviour, but he does not cry in order to receive comfort, he cries because he is uncomfortable. Out of sight is out of mind, and his attention at nine months is easily diverted from one object to another. What is in his hand or his mouth is part of himself—not until he reaches out to grasp an object and can relinquish it at will can he perceive that the object is *not* part of him.

About his first birthday the child begins to make useful associations. He now knows that mother still exists, even if she is out of the room, and will come if he cries.

One to Four Years

The imitative behaviour of a child of this age leads to his appearing to know more than he does. He presses a switch: the light comes on. No conception of electrical circuits enters his mind, only the pragmatic connection between " light " and " switch ". This form of thinking by association is termed " syncretic ", and precedes the power to link cause and effect through logical reasoning. Developing speech makes it possible for him to symbolise some simple concepts for interior consideration; but this young child will often act out his ideas in play rather than meditate on them.

He is still supremely egocentric and believes that the existence of all other objects is contingent upon his perception. He endows his environment with his own characteristics; that is, his ideas are animistic or anthropomorphic. If he bumps into a table, the table is " naughty " to have hurt him.

He categorises very crudely: all women are mummies and all four-legged animals are bow-wows or pussies, according to which is the more familiar to him. The doctor's own child thinks all men (milkmen included) work in hospitals. All his ideas are absolutely concrete: heaven is a real place with grass, flowers and toys, God is daddy, only larger and older.

Four to Seven Years

The child can now more and more often substitute imagined activity for the real thing, and does not always clearly distinguish between fantasy and reality. He is now better able to accept that events can happen without his taking part in them, that there was even a time before he was born, and there will be a future perhaps after he is dead. His reasoning is still anthropomorphic; he feels that man is responsible for everything and asks " Who makes the sea go in and out? " " Who built the cliff? "

Seven Years Onwards

Great advances are now made in the power of classification, and he begins to deal with abstract concepts. He achieves some understanding of " number " as distinct from counting, " space " as distinct from measurement, and " time " as more than the gap between one meal and the next. Syncretism begins to wane, and logical explanation begins to assume its real importance. At six " a bicycle goes along because a man is sitting on it ". At seven or eight " a bicycle goes along because a man is riding it, turning the pedals to make the wheels go round ". The child is now less certain of the validity of his deductions and prefaces remarks with " I think " or " Perhaps ". He will not now accept simple explanations so readily; he wishes to test them out for himself. He begins to make use of other people's reasoning powers and experience to extend his own range.

In Adolescence

The boy or girl begins to find interest in abstractions of every kind. He begins to realise that some questions cannot be answered by even the brightest of his teachers. and indeed that there may be some questions that will never be answered by anyone. He will look for logical explanations in preference to anthropomorphic ones and has a respect for scientific method. For much of the time he is willing to believe that other people know more then he does, and have a right to think differently from himself on controversial topics. He also understands the nature of useful approximations. The recurring decimal place, the inexactitude of π and the manipulations of calculus are cheerfully accepted for their practical value.

SELECTED BIBLIOGRAPHY

1. *The Natural Development of the Child.* Bowley, A. E. 1957. London: Livingstone. This describes individual emotional development.
2. *Child Care and the Growth of Love.* Bowlby, J. 1953. London: Pelican. This book and the next two deal with maternal deprivation.
3. *Young Children in Hospital.* Robertson, J. 1958. London: Tavistock Publications.
4. *Hospitals and Children: A Parents' Eye View.* Robertson, J. 1962. London: Gollancz.
5. *Baby and Child Care.* Spock, B. 1958. London: Bodley Head.
6. *The Growth of Logical Thinking.* Inhelder, B. and Piaget, J. 1958. U.S.A.: Basic Books Inc. An account of the development of reasoning in children.

Chapter 18

ADOLESCENCE, MATURITY AND OLD AGE

Emotional Growth in Adolescence

There is a marked tendency in our Society at the present day to regard adolescence as a time of trial and to see individual boys or girls from twelve to twenty as dangerous young animals, quite different in every way from the children they were before puberty or the adults they will be (legally, at least) after they reach their twenty-first birthdays. This is a grossly distorted view of an exciting and important time of life, seen largely through the distorting lens of rigid attitudes in a culture largely dominated by middle-aged and elderly people. It is also a dangerous view in so far as it suggests that " teenagers " must either be placated at all costs, and their enthusiasms allowed to dominate the social scene, or that they must be suppressed at all costs and made to feel their relative impotence on every occasion. Either attitude does harm because it prevents that free assessment of individual by individual without which no worthwhile personal relationship can be achieved.

Tanner has written " Perhaps one of the chief clues to adolescence lies in the fact that at that time the potentialities for many various kinds of behaviour are still present. Mutually incompatible drives and emotions are simultaneously aroused, many of which later become shed or repressed bit by bit as the individual chooses inevitably this path rather than that, and increasingly limits the range of his response."

Biological Factors in Adolescence

There is increasing mental ability with a growth in the power to make and use abstractions, and to pose questions demanding extensive reference to the experience of others for their answers. Side by side with this goes increasing height, physical power, and adult appearance as shown by the acquisition of body hair and the configuration of facial bones. These are gradual occurrences which do not startle or overwhelm the individual boy or girl; but the sudden upsurge of sexual interest and drive that comes with the maturation of sex glands in both girls and boys can be alarming and girls especially may be disturbed at the menarche. The strong sexual urge of adolescents may in itself account for their assertive and sometimes aggressive behaviour towards others, but it is possible that general endocrinal changes contribute to their drive for independence and authority.

Cultural Factors

These generally act in such a way as to thwart the new assertiveness of the adolescent, just as the family demanded, and generally obtained some degree of submission from the rapidly developing toddler. *Economic* dependence on the family usually persists through early adolescence and is prolonged where vocational or professional training is sought: sometimes the family's authority may be replaced or augmented by the authority of teachers, and of such statutory bodies as education authorities, college governers, and the foreman at work; even when a boy leaves school at the earliest permitted age and begins to make his own contribution to the housekeeping money, he cannot achieve full independence; his own lack of experience will lead him to make mistakes that have to be rectified by others. All the same there is no doubt that adolescence is less stressful where it is possible for the growing boy or girl to feel himself a useful and self-respecting member of the household. In working-class homes a girl may, for instance, go to work in a shop at fifteen or sixteen. She will give her mother some of her wages, help her a little in her spare time, begin to court seriously by eighteen, and probably marry before she is twenty. The opportunities for parents and daughter to clash are reduced in these circumstances. A girl from a similar background whose unusual intellectual ability won her a place at a University would find her life far more difficult; her parents' pride at her success would conflict with their natural wish for her to make some economic contribution to the house, it might be difficult for them to accept that time spent reading in her home represented necessary work and should excuse her from household chores, and last but not least, should she show a normal interest in sex and acquire a boy friend, they might reproach her for " throwing away her chances ". Again the adolescent who was once a naturally submissive child and is now growing up in a home where parental authority is never relaxed and supervision is continuous and strict, is more likely to show explosive misconduct at this age, than the boy or girl in a more liberal home where individuals are highly respected and trusted and more has been left to the young person's own conscience.

Postponement of Needs

Where young people cannot support themselves, let alone a wife and family, and must postpone their longing for freedom and sexual

gratification, we observe certain patterns of behaviour. These include:
A great increase in daydreaming and fantasy.

Emotional instability not unlike that of the toddler's years, tender affectionate behaviour alternating with overt hostility or withdrawn, sullen silence.

Substitutive interests, which cover a vast range of activities from simple masturbation as a substitute for heterosexual experience, to the religious and political interests of adolescence. Preoccupation with dress is common, and a restless search for amusement leads boys and girls to every sort of social venue.

Rebellion against Society, which is seen as the thwarting agency. This may take such mild forms as neglect or eccentricity of dress, or may be more disturbing as when a boy truants, steals, fights with intent to hurt, destroys property, or experiments sexually without regard to the responsibilities and risks involved. A girl's rebellion is more likely to be obviously sexual, but other forms of misconduct do occur.

There is a tendency to relate all concepts to the individual; that is to say, all ideas are examined from his or her standpoint and accepted or rejected in the same rather narrow way. " What's in it for me? " is an understandable reaction in young people who see the world around them arranged—or so it must seem—for the exclusive benefit of older people who can spend money, enjoy sex, and plan their future without constantly submitting their choices for adult scrutiny and approval.

The late developer, who starts the race to maturity behind his peers is often made to feel inferior to them, as each friend in turn achieves facial hair, a deep voice and the power to masturbate ahead of him. His childish appearance may lead to his being treated by his parents as if he were younger than he actually is, and this in turn saps his none too great confidence. He may become preoccupied with his physique: or a determination to show himself the equal of more mature boys may lead to bellicose and exhibitionistic behaviour. Finally, he may develop very suddenly and rapidly in late adolescence, sometimes outstripping the early developers. To become " Lanky " after being " Titch " for years only exacerbates his self-consciousness and upsets him still further. These problems are not so marked in girls, as parents are seldom so bothered by the idea of a girl's being small and childish in appearance as they may be by doubts about a son's being adequately virile.

Maturity

We have already discussed, in the first section of Chapter 17, some aspects of mature behaviour as we understand it. In general it may be said that the adult man between twenty-five and seventy shows himself largely in his social role of provider for his wife and children and worker in the field for which his talents and opportunities have fitted him. Marriage, and even more, the rearing of a family will make it increasingly difficult for him to make a choice or take a stand on issues which involve possible suffering to those dependent on him, and so will his own increasing wish for comfort and peace. If his career has involved a long period of training with prolonged postponement of other satisfactions he will hope to find in it reasonable material reward and sustaining daily interest; a wise choice of marriage partner and a family within his means to support will contribute to his general well-being and hence to his reluctance to accept much change in his life. He is increasingly unlikely to welcome new ideas or take up new enthusiasms, except marginal ones which may safely be labelled " hobbies ". What he is losing in freedom of choice and flexibility of outlook he can however be gaining in a sense of worth: the dependence of others on his continued powers may worry him but also increases his self-regard. He becomes experienced, and perhaps " expert " at his daily work, with all the satisfaction that that implies, and is richly rewarded for his patience and steady behaviour by the love of his wife and the goodwill (often slightly amused) of his children. The mature woman during her sexual life may choose to have few or many children, and has at least some power to arrange this according to her wishes. If she has special abilities, she may be able to work out of her home after her children reach school age or when they leave home; or she may, if she is more domestically minded, find full satisfaction in creating and maintaining a beautiful and happy home. She is more likely than her husband to be lonely and bored, especially when her children are very young and represent—however dearly she may love them—more of a tie than a pleasure: but she has learned to subdue her needs and wishes to theirs and to find her own fulfilment in providing the conditions for their happy growth. If she is wise, she will be ready to let them enjoy independence as soon as they are able to fend for themselves, and when they finally leave home she will stay on good terms with them and welcome the new interest brought into her life by their marriage partners and the arrival of grandchildren.

Both men and women in these years will often suffer setbacks and disappointments, and their capacity to deal with these and not to become embittered is a highly individual matter. Ill-health, war, poverty or failure can come to anybody and alter the picture of their lives in every way. Not the least significant sign of maturity may be the capacity to foresee difficulties and dangers and to take reasonable precautions to forestall them. To look ahead to old age and make some provision to deal with leisure and a reduced income is one aspect of this foresight.

Senescence and Senility

Since most of those reading this book will live to be seventy years old, many to be eighty, and some at least will see their ninetieth birthday, there is very good reason to examine current attitudes to old age and attempt to separate those qualities which properly belong to it from those which are purely adventitious.

The old people among us today often present a disturbing and disheartening picture. Many of them grew up in poverty and suffered diseases in childhood, such as rickets, pneumonia and rheumatism which have left them permanently damaged. Some may have lost sons in the two world wars, or voluntarily restricted the size of their families in the economic depression of the twenties and thirties, so that they now lack children and grandchildren to satisfy their emotional needs and supply them with interest as well as financial help. The poverty of some made it impossible to save for the future; others are living on small fixed incomes deemed adequate thirty years ago but shrinking yearly as prices rise. The basic pension allowed by the Welfare State is barely adequate even for a restricted life, and the need to depend on other people's charity for a few little pleasures and luxuries is a great hardship for people who have always prided themselves on their independence. The picture, then, is frequently an unhappy one; old age is blurred and marred by illness, by poverty, by loneliness and by boredom and idleness; above all, by a terrible sense of having no value in anyone's eyes.

A different picture emerges when these extraneous factors are removed. A married couple ageing together with an income adequate to their needs, with children who welcome their occasional visits, and see to it that they are welcome at family occasions—these two, given reasonable health, may well consider themselves blessed. Their responsibilities and anxieties have declined, they have ample time for hobbies and can be together more than perhaps ever before. If their income is large enough to permit travel and domestic help they may be as happy—or a great deal happier—than many younger people.

Let us say, then, that the environment profoundly modifies the changes of old age, and that physical and economic handicaps increase loneliness and boredom and lead often to eccentric and socially unpleasant behaviour. Beneath this overlay (see Chapter 19) the basic changes leading to senility are as follows:

An actual, measurable *decline in intelligence* as assessed by standard psychometric tests (see Chapter 5).

A poor ability to retain newly learned material though old memories are comparatively well retained (see Chapter 4).

A gradual " shutting down " of interests and activities, often because of increasing physical weakness.

Changes occur in the sexual powers and inclinations of old people. Although most men and women experience a waning of sexual interests in old age, some still feel strong sexual passion and this can be a great source of suffering where a marriage partner has been lost. .

Deafness, decreasing visual acuity and disturbances of posture and joint function short of actual arthritis hamper the enjoyment of old age and are so common as to be regarded as truly part of the total picture.

Emotional Regression

Very old people are often extremely and cheerfully selfish, reacting with tantrums and grief to any delay in the meeting of their demands: this is the origin of the phrase " second childhood ". In contrast with the adventurousness of childhood and its urge to independence is the increasing timidity of the aged, varied from time to time by truculent assertiveness.

Dis-inhibition

Abnormalities of personality which have been well concealed during adult life are now sometimes seen revealed, as the control necessary to compensate for or conceal unacceptable traits slackens. The unusual person may become an out-and-out eccentric, the woman who has been indifferent to fashion frankly dowdy and even dirty.

Those who attend the old need as much wisdom and patience as those who attend the young. Much might be learned from a study of those Societies where the old are respected partly at least on account of their age. The function of old people as a repository of stored knowledge and experience has vanished with the advance of technology and the use of means of communication more permanent—and reliable —than human speech. But it need not be beyond the powers of our culture to find a place where the abilities of the old may be brought into use so as to entitle them—in their own eyes—to the respect we would all wish them to enjoy.

SELECTED BIBLIOGRAPHY

1. *Growth in Adolescence.* Tanner, J. 1962. Oxford: Blackwell.
   This is a comprehensive view of the subject.
2. *He and She.* Barnes, K. 1962: London: Penguin Handbook.
   This little book is a well-informed discussion of the psychological, social and physiological aspects of sexual behaviour.

Chapter 19

PSYCHOLOGICAL REACTIONS TO ILLNESS AND TREATMENT

Introduction

Illnesses of any sort comprise one of the great fears or threats to human beings. Most people plan for the future on the basis of their present physical and mental abilities and their past experience of the use of these abilities in satisfying their needs. Any illness which alters, however temporarily, the physical and mental abilities of a patient upsets his capacity to foresee and plan for the future and this gives rise to anxieties and worries with which he will have to deal.

In an acute illness of short duration the psychological problems are seldom serious or difficult to deal with. A typical case might be as follows: a young married man with children arrives home from work feeling feverish and " off colour ". He goes to bed, has a very restless night and wakes up in the morning with a severe pain in his chest and an unpleasant cough. Even by this stage he may have developed certain fears and worries. He may fear death or permanent incapacity resulting in financial disaster for his family. However, before these fears get a hold and work on his confused and toxic mind the doctor has been and reassured him that the illness is a mild attack of pneumonia which is easy to treat and cure. Similarly his wife is calmed and when, after three to five days, one of the antibiotics has the desired effect and the patient begins to feel well again, little is left of the original fears.

In a physically ill patient the best psychotherapy is to cure the organic disease and restore the patient to full physical and mental health. In an acute illness such as pneumonia there is no real problem. However, in any illness that lasts more than a few weeks the problem is more complex and difficult to tackle.

The psychological state of the ill patient is the result of a whole set of factors operating before, during and after the illness. These factors have different impacts on different patients and different end results.

Age of Onset and Duration of Illness

Early Childhood

Illness occurring at this period of life tends to reduce the child's contacts with his environment. Because of this, the chronically ill

179

child sometimes shows a picture of intellectual backwardness, due to lack of adequate mental and physical stimulation.

It is easy to see how the blind and deaf child may have difficulty in learning from the environment. Indeed the idea that a deaf child will also be dumb has become part of the folk-lore of Western civilisation. Nevertheless, it is fairly rare for a child born deaf to be unable to speak because of any physical defect. At one time congenitally deaf children did not speak because, being unable to hear the human voice, they had no opportunity of imitating sounds or using sounds as a means of communication. It was because of this that they appeared intellectually backward and indeed after the passage of many years tended to become so. Nowadays, deaf children are taught to speak by special methods and the deaf and dumb child is becoming a rarity.

A child who has to lie in bed for long periods may not be able to use his arms and hands to manipulate toys, bricks, cups, and so on. Because of this he may have great difficulty in learning the size and shape of objects and how to co-ordinate limb and eye movements. Such children may appear intellectually backward.

Apart from intellectual backwardness the whole of the child's personality tends to develop more slowly. The ill child remains very dependent upon his parents or upon those adults taking his parents' place. He will tend to retain childish habits for very much longer and may resume other childish habits he was thought to have grown out of at an earlier age. This regression of emotional development tends to be especially severe in those children whose illnesses necessitate their being confined to bed for long periods of time. Some of these children tend to retain childish immature patterns of emotional response in adult life (see Chapter 17).

Adult Life

Illnesses occurring in the adult will have very different consequences. Adults are not as plastic as children, they cannot adapt themselves to new conditions as easily and the older a patient gets the less is his capacity for adjustment. Chronic illness may necessitate the patient's changing his whole way of life. The older the patient, the more difficult it becomes for him to adapt to a new mode of living especially if this involves any limitation or change of occupation. A clerk who develops a disability of his right hand or a manual worker who develops a coronary thrombosis may have very difficult problems of readjustment. These people frequently develop severe feelings of frustration and uselessness.

Involvement of the Central Nervous System

In illnesses which involve the central nervous system the psychological effect will not only depend upon the personality of the patient, and how he reacts to the effects of the illness, but also upon the direct changes which the illness may bring about in the patient's personality and mental capacity.

Damage to the brain can be caused in many ways such as direct traumatic injury, growths, blockage to the arterial supply, and nutritional deficiencies. However the actual damage is caused, the psychological effects tend to be similar. These psychological changes are described below.

Memory Impairment

Disease affecting the brain produces a particular type of memory disturbance. These have been described in Chapters 4 and 6, where it was noted that remote memories are less vulnerable to loss than recent ones. Patients suffering from long-standing and slowly progressive damage to the brain will be able to remember in great detail all about their childhood but will be unable to remember what they had for breakfast or who they saw yesterday. Some of these patients seem able to compensate for a while by keeping an elaborate notebook into which all events and facts are meticulously entered. This type of memory disturbance affects just as much the man in his early thirties suffering from a severe head injury as it does the old man in his seventies with a poor arterial supply to his brain.

Intellectual Impairment

The patient's ability to perform intellectual tasks of all sorts is diminished, although some tasks are performed worse than others. He tends to tire easily in tasks involving abstract thought, and he becomes slow and muddled in tackling even simple problems (see Chapter 3). When the brain damage is not very great his store of words and general information is not greatly affected but as the illness progresses he tends to become verbose and repetitive although the size of his vocabulary decreases. Sometimes, if the illness is very severe, he develops delusions and may think he is being persecuted by communists or the police. These delusions are partly caused by impaired contact with, and the lack of understanding of, the environment (see Chapter 12).

Emotional Changes

In the early stages of the illness or when the brain damage is slight, some patients develop severe anxiety and depression especially when they realise that they are losing abilities they had previously. However, this stage does not last very long and the emotional changes may then take several different forms. A few patients become euphoric, naïve, talkative and sociable in a childish way, others become apathetic, slow and ponderous in both speech and movement. Most patients develop pronounced mood swings. At one moment they may be smiling and happy and a few minutes later they will be miserable and tearful. These moods may be interspersed by outbursts of irritability and bad temper.

Character Changes

Perhaps the most distressing aspects to the family are seen in character changes. In these there tends to be a loss of acquired social inhibitions. Patients who have hitherto led conventional and blameless lives may suddenly start to indulge in sexual misbehaviour or petty crime. They may become tactless in speech and slovenly in ' dress. Occasionally they end up in court charged with some antisocial offence such as shoplifting or indecent exposure.

Confusional States in Acute Illness

Apart from actual damage to the brain any condition that effectively interferes with the functioning of the brain for a short period can give rise to direct psychological effects. In acute respiratory diseases the oxygen supply to the brain may be temporarily diminished or in infectious diseases toxins may interfere with the normal physiology of the brain. These conditions have similar psychological effects to those already described. They are, however, short-lived and fluctuate in intensity. Memory defects, and intellectual impairment tend to make the patient very frightened. He may become confused, especially at night, and may develop dream-like states in which he imagines he sees people and animals. This leads to disorientation in time and place such as described in Chapter 12.

The degree to which a patient reacts to any of these psychological disabilities depends upon the stability of his previous personality.

Condition of the Patient Before the Onset of the Illness

The patient's personality, physical condition and psychological situation can all play a part in determining the nature of his psychological reaction to his illness.

Personality

Intelligence plays a large part in the ability of any person to adjust to illness. Patients of poor intelligence sometimes find that the situation produced by the illness is too complex for them to handle. In hospital these patients become very dependent on the medical and nursing staff. They tend to lose any initiative they may have had although their child-like attitude makes them popular with the staff. When the acute stage of their illness is over and they leave hospital they often need sympathetic encouragement to get them back to work and a normal mode of living. If they develop a permanent disability some of them sink into states of apathy and despair broken periodically by outbursts of temper. They then need careful rehabilitation to help them readjust to the new situation.

The emotional maturity and stability of the patient is also of prime importance. Patients with a high capacity to tolerate psychological and physical stress can usually adjust to illness without difficulty, whereas a patient who has been over-protected in childhood may find himself ill-equipped to deal with the psychological stresses involved. If the patient's situation is such that he is still overprotected by his parents when he develops the illness he may easily slip into a state of chronic invalidism. If, however, he is now on his own, a reaction of irritability leading eventually to a mood of despondency is more common. Not only the overprotected, but also the patient whose childhood upbringing was erratic because his parents were absent, incompetent or unstable, may also find difficulty in coping with chronic illness.

Physical Condition

Any patient's ability to adjust to an illness will obviously depend upon his physical fitness prior to the onset of the illness. The fitter the patient was before the illness the less will be the actual disability produced by the illness and the easier will the patient overcome any handicap that results.

Patient's Actual Psychological Situation

The psychological environment in which the patient becomes ill or is injured occasionally carries a symbolic meaning for that patient. An actual clinical case will perhaps illustrate this type of reaction. A married woman with two grown-up children had a husband who was a salesman, away from home for twelve days out of fourteen. One day, when peeling potatoes, she stabbed the palm of her right hand, and over the next few days developed a severe palmar infection which necessitated her admission to hospital for a few days for a minor operation. During the convalescent period the skin and tissues of the palm became fibrosed and she developed a " claw hand ". Physiotherapy and rehabilitation produced very little progress and the condition remained stationary. During the period of the patient's hospitalisation and rehabilitation the family had rallied round magnificently. The husband had managed to cut his periods away from home to four days per fortnight and the children used to take turns to stay at home in the evening to keep their mother company. She no longer felt neglected and isolated. Due to her illness she felt she was wanted again. The psychological situation was however even more complicated. The patient was the youngest of three children. She had always been very close to her father emotionally. He had been wounded in the right arm during the First World War and had been left with a partially paralysed right arm and hand. The patient was thus managing to recapture the emotions of a very happy period of her life, which were fortified by the rallying round of her family.

A different type of reaction can be seen in patients with coronary thrombosis. It is unlikely that coronary thrombosis is primarily caused by psychological factors. Physical factors such as inheritance, exercise and diet are probably more important. Coronary thrombosis can, however, be precipitated by psychological stress, especially when the other factors are present. It is not uncommon for coronary thrombosis to occur during or just after a strong emotional reaction of anger, frustration or self-reproach. These reactions can be especially severe in driving, conscientious people, who take their work very seriously.

The Psychological Response of the Patient to Therapeutic Drugs

It is well known that substances which have no direct chemical action on the body can be used to influence the course of an illness. These pharmacologically inactive substances are used on a large scale by doctors all over the world to treat both mental and physical illnesses. It is becoming more widely realised that not only do these inert substances produce subjective changes in the patient, but also changes in their physiological state via the autonomic nervous system and the endocrine glands. These inert substances are known as *placebos*.

Types of Placebo Response

To observe the types of response obtained by giving placebos two criteria need to be fulfilled in both experimental and clinical work.

(a) The patient must not know that the drug is inert, indeed he should think he is having an active substance. As most people have a steadfast faith in drugs, the first criterion is easy to fulfil.

(b) The doctor (or whoever happens to be the observer) must also be unaware that the substance is pharmacologically inert.

Both criteria can be fully satisfied by using a technique of drug trial called a *double blind trial*. A drug trial reported in the *British Medical Journal* by Leak and Julian (*B.M.J.*, June 9, 1962) illustrates this technique. Twenty-eight patients with well-established heart disease giving rise to severe pain on exertion were selected. The double blind trial was designed so that each patient would receive successive six-week courses of therapy with iproniazid, nialamide, meprobamate and a placebo in random order. This resulted in each patient's acting as his own control. The results were statistically analysed. Leak and Julian took as their criteria of an excellent response a reduction in the number of attacks of pain to 25% of the average level. There were three excellent responses on iproniazid, three on nialamide and three on meprobamate, but the most striking result from our point of view were the four excellent responses obtained with the placebo alone. That is 14% of the patients showed striking relief from organically determined pain when given an inert substance.

Beecher and his colleagues in the U.S.A., who have done so much work on this problem, attempted to determine the magnitude of the therapeutic effect of placebos. They did this by adding together the placebo responses in fifteen drug trials involving 1082 patients. They found that 35% showed marked improvement on the inert substance alone.

Not only do placebos produce beneficial results, but like other therapeutic agents they have associated toxic effects. Some of these side effects observed by Beecher are shown below.

Percentage of Patients Showing Side Effects of Placebos

Dry mouth	9%
Nausea	10%
Headaches	25%
Drowsiness	50%
Fatigue	18%
Sleepiness	10%

There is a remarkable similarity between these side effects and the side effects of some of the newer antidepressant drugs.

Little is known of the exact mechanism whereby an inert substance can affect the physiology of the body. Cleghorn studied these effects on adrenal cortex function in neurotic patients with severe anxiety. When he gave these patients an intramuscular injection of isotonic saline the neutrophil count increased, the lymphocytes and eosinophils decreased, the serum sodium increased and the serum potassium decreased. This marked increase in adrenocortical activity was probably due to the increased secretion of corticotrophin by the anterior part of the pituitary gland.

Personality of Individuals and the Conditions under which they Respond to Placebos

Not much is known of the differences between those individuals who produce marked responses to placebos and those that produce little or no response. Those who respond are usually called *placebo reactors* and those who do not, *placebo non-reactors*.

Some light has been shed on the problem by a study of patients suffering from post-operative pain. The active drug used in this study was morphine phosphate and the placebo, isotonic saline. Half the patients obtained marked relief from the placebo alone compared with 70% from morphine. The placebo was most effective when the pain was intense but of short duration and there was evidence that the placebo effect diminished with the passage of time. These patients were given extensive psychological tests and psychiatric interviews. Differences were found between placebo reactors and non-reactors. In general, placebo reactors after operation became very dependent on the doctors and nursing staff. They had great faith in the treatment and derived comfort from becoming child-like again and letting the staff deal with their problems. The non-reactors tended to be very independent and rather withdrawn. They clung rigidly to what they thought was a critical attitude to their treatment. It is, however, uncertain that these are the only personality differences or that they occur in most cases.

Conditions in which the Optimum Placebo Response Occurs

Many years ago a psychologist, Elton Mayo, studying the conditions of work at the Hawthorne plant of the Western Electric Company, in America, discovered some interesting facts which have a bearing on the present problem. He was interested in the degree of illumination and its effect on the work output. As the illumination in one shop was increased, so the output increased. At the end of the experiment the illumination was decreased to its original level and to his surprise the output of the shop continued to rise. After a further series of careful experiments Elton Mayo came to the conclusion that any change in the environment, good, bad or indifferent, would lead to an increase in output, if the workers felt that the management was taking a direct interest in their well-being and making the change for their benefit. A similar principle can be applied to the relationship between the patient and his doctor. Any change in the environment that the doctor brings about will produce an improvement in the patient's condition if he believes that the doctor is bringing about the change for his benefit. The converse will also apply. The actual degree of improvement depends upon the condition from which the patient is suffering, the personality of the patient, the personality of the doctor and the relationship between the two. From this it can be seen that the response of a patient to a new drug will partly depend upon the enthusiasm and faith of the doctor in that drug and the degree to which he can communicate his enthusiasm to the patient.

This last statement has been tested clinically by Lasagna. A drug investigation involving 120 psycho-neurotic inpatients was initiated. It appeared to the patients, nurses and doctors that a new tranquilliser and a new energiser were to be evaluated. In actual fact both drugs were placebos. With the placebo (called a tranquilliser) there was improvement in 56% of the patients. With the placebo (called an energiser) only 40% of the patients improved. Not only the quantity but the type of improvement varied with the different placebos. With the tranquilliser, half the patients felt more relaxed and several complained of drowsiness. With the energiser, a quarter felt more cheerful and active and none felt drowsy. When the attitude of the doctors to the placebos was examined it was found they had more confidence in the tranquilliser and that they felt the energiser was a less suitable drug for that type of patient.

There is no doubt that not only do the actions of drugs in human beings vary according to the psychological and social conditions, but also in animals. Clance found that the lethal dose of Amphetamine in mice depended upon whether they were solitary or in groups. (The lethal dose resulting in 50% of the mice being killed was 117 mg. per kilogram of body weight in solitary mice, and only 14 mg. per kilogram of body weight when the mice were together in groups of ten.)

It can thus be seen that there are three factors in the action of any therapeutic drug.

1. A direct chemical effect on the body.
2. An indirect physiological effect. This is produced by the emotional changes that take place in the patient acting on the autonomic nervous system and the endocrine glands.
3. A direct psychological effect via the doctor-patient relationship.

Social Situation

The stability of the social situation and especially of the primary groups such as the family and the place of work can affect the manner and the degree to which the patient reacts to his illness.

In patients who belong to closely knit families the psychological reaction to illness can be limited. These families rally round their ill

member and give him all the support he needs. Once the acute stage
is over the support should not be uncritical. They must help the
patient to convalesce by means of encouragement. Too much uncritical sympathy at this stage can lead the emotionally immature
patient into chronic invalidism. This is frequently seen in the over-
anxious mother with a small family. The children of these mothers
especially after any moderately serious illness tend to get labelled
" delicate " even when there is no longer any medical evidence to
show that they are less robust than their schoolmates.

Long periods of stay in hospital can break the relationship between
the patient and his family. It tends to contract his horizons, making
him dependent once again. In hospital he is not only discouraged to
do things for himself, he is actively encouraged to become dependent
on the ward staff. He is only allowed to do things for himself or for
others when this does not interfere with the ward routine. He gets used
to making no decisions and having everything planned out for him.
He is back in an environment similar in some ways to that of his
childhood, and occasionally he regresses to childish modes of behaviour.
To some extent this effect of hospitalisation is beneficial, especially in
acute illness. The acutely ill patient feels unable to cope with the
world and is only too glad when the staff relieve him of all his worries.
However in long-term illness hospitalisation has psychological dis-
advantages. The patient becomes dependent and self-centred. When
he is discharged his family may continue the same excessive support
and gradually the whole household revolves around the patient's
illness, real or imaginary. Other families react in the opposite way by
rejecting the patient. Indeed it is a common experience of doctors
working with chronically ill patients in hospital to find that the relatives
will not have the patient home.

Not only does the family have an effect on the patient but the patient
affects his family. When the husband is ill there may be a considerable increase in household work. The wife may find that she
has to make all the decisions, works longer hours and has less relaxation.
There may be financial difficulties which leads to other members of
the family having to go out to work. Family holidays may have to be
curtailed. Some wives under this type of stress develop mild psychiatric
illnesses. When the wife is ill the husband may be overworked. The
financial difficulties are less severe but if there are young children the
husband may have to employ domestic help, and this is costly. Children
too, become worried and depressed when their parents are ill for long,
and the home routine is disrupted.

Time Interval Between Onset Treatment and Rehabilitation

The actual time interval between the realisation by the patient and his doctor that he has a chronic illness and the onset of his treatment and rehabilitation has a considerable influence on the eventual outlook. If the period is too long the psychological overlay will tend to be excessive and persist after the treatment has been completed. Experience in the U.S.A. and other countries suggests that if the time interval is greater than three years, secondary psychological reactions are likely to prove intractable. This is especially so when injuries are likely to involve financial compensation as a result of legal action.

SELECTED BIBLIOGRAPHY

1. *Psychological Aspects of Clinical Medicine*. Barton Hall, S. 1949. London: H. K. Lewis.
2. "The Powerful Placebo". Beecher, H. K. 1955. *Jour. Amer. Med. Ass.* 1602.

Chapter 20

INTERPERSONAL RELATIONSHIPS IN THE HOSPITAL

Role Playing

Whenever two or more people meet, the sort of social interchange that develops will largely be determined by the role each person is playing in the situation. This role, in turn, will be determined partly by the person himself: what he sees himself as; and partly by other people in the situation: the role they see him in, or the role they cast for him. This sort of thing is, of course, reciprocal, we tend to play the role allotted to us by others, and others to some extent react to us accordingly to the role we are playing.

Many, if not most of the people we meet, are perceived and reacted to by us, not so much as people in their own right, but as players of roles. We react not so much to John Smith or Mary Jones, as to the bank-clerk, the postman, the policewoman and the shop-assistant. Nowhere is this so obvious as in a hospital, and to a lesser extent in the doctor's surgery.

There are at least seven distinct roles in the complex organisation of a hospital. These are the doctor role, the nurse role, the medical auxiliary role, the social worker role, the domestic worker role, the patient role and the patient's relative role. These are quite distinct, although not always seen as such by the patient. It is common, for example, for patients to cast any man wearing a white coat in the doctor role. Within each type of role there is, of course, a strictly observed hierarchy, stretching from the senior consultant to the medical student, and from the matron to the junior probationer nurse. This stratification may impair communication between people at the various levels within one type of role, as much as between people playing different roles. We shall return to this topic later.

Administrators and others connected with the National Health Service are becoming increasingly concerned about the relationships between the operators of the Service: the doctors, nurses and so on; and the users: the patients and their relatives. One particular problem which has been mentioned repeatedly in the literature is that of *communication*: not only between the doctor and the patient, but between the doctor and the nurse, and between the doctor and his own medical colleagues.

Interpersonal relationships among human beings depend on efficient communication between them much of which is non-verbal. The way a person walks or stands, the kind of clothes he wears, and particularly, of course, his facial expression, are all potent methods of making non-verbal statements of what sort of person he is, what mood he is in, whether he approves or disapproves of what is going on and so on. A white coat with a stethoscope sticking out of the pocket is a non-verbal statement that the wearer is a doctor. After a ward round, patients quite often say " The doctor seemed pleased ", or " He looked worried " or " He was sympathetic " or " He had no time for me to-day "; while they can say little or nothing of what the doctor actually *said*.

The respective roles played by people will produce well-defined expectations and patterns of behaviour which in turn determine what is said, when, and by whom and to whom. Later in this chapter we shall consider some specific relationships between various people taking the different hospital roles, and we shall see what effects they have on what is said, or on the efficiency of the communication taking place. These expectations produce *mental sets* which predispose people to notice certain factors in the situation, to ignore others, and to make decisions along certain lines expected of them. We saw in Chapter 2 that a perceiver's mental set would predispose him to see a situation in one particular way rather than in any other. These expectations and mental sets may prevent effective communication from taking place.

An example is as follows: a patient had been attending an out-patient clinic for back-ache and had been seeing the appropriate orthopaedic consultant. He had been given the proper treatment for his symptoms as then known. On one occasion a medical officer was doing the clinic who, having plenty of time that day, allowed the patient to ramble on about his symptoms. It then appeared that the patient was also getting a good deal of rectal discharge which appeared to him to contain blood and pus. A rectal examination revealed a tumour which had been giving him the back-ache. There are two points of interest here relevant to the failure of communication. The patient, when asked why he had not told the doctor about his other symptoms, said that he had not been asked, and did not think in any case that they had anything to do with his back pain. The second of these statements could have been perfectly true; after all patients are not expected to be medically sophisticated. It seems unlikely, however, that the patient was not, in fact, asked about his other symptoms. It is much more probable that he was alarmed and frightened about his abnormal bowel movements and was afraid to mention them, knowing that they might well be highly relevant, but putting off the evil day when they would have to be faced up to and dealt with. It is important to realise that quite often the patient is not wittingly being untruthful. Sometimes he cannot remember to mention symptoms which alarm him, because at the moment he is asked about them, he has actually forgotten them. Thus when the doctor says: " Have you any other symptoms? " or he may even say " Have you noticed anything unusual about your bowel movements? " the patient may answer "No, Doctor, it's only my back that hurts." He may well have repressed the unpleasant symptoms which he would so much rather forget. It is only when he rambles on in a sort of " free-association " way that he remembers the things that he ought to mention. Many doctors have commented on the fact that patients sometimes tell them the one vital piece of information about themselves as they are going out of the surgery door.

This refusal of a frightened patient to face up to unpleasant facts or even to be able to remember them when asked, is known as *perceptual defence*. The same sort of thing can occur in the doctor who has made a firm diagnosis on which he has staked his professional reputation, and who is then unable to perceive any data which contraindicate it. In one study 231 patients were told clearly that they had a curable form of cancer, and a month later 43 of them denied categorically that they had been so informed. Patients' relatives, too, can exhibit perpetual defence when they are anxious and upset. In one case a woman was told clearly that her husband was very ill and might die. When the patient did in fact die a week later, his wife upbraided the doctor for not warning her that this might happen. In this case the wife might not have taken in the unpleasant information, or having done so might have promptly repressed it.

Another process, known as *verbal conditioning*, may also impair communication. A person being interviewed can unwittingly be encouraged to produce information of a certain type, or in a certain area of enquiry, and be discouraged from talking about things the interviewer does not wish to hear about, or is not interested in. This is something over and above the natural desire of any interviewer to keep the patient to the point. It happens when a doctor very naturally shows more interest in some types of statements than others, and thus unwittingly encourages the patient to produce more of the interest-producing remarks and to inhibit the sort of statements that seems not to produce a response in the doctor. If a doctor shows an interest in a certain type of symptom or pays particular attention to information in a certain area, the patient is inclined to talk about these matters to the exclusion of others.

Communication Between Doctors

Doctors with a specialist training and interests necessarily develop mental sets which predispose them to notice certain features of their patients and ignore or simply not notice others. A surgeon examining a patient will look for operable conditions, and a psychiatrist for mental symptoms. It is unfortunately true that sometimes a patient with vague and undefined aches and pains will do the round of physicians and surgeons and will receive a series of diagnoses, each in terms of the speciality of the doctor making it. Such patients may receive a variety of treatments from physicians, have several organs removed by surgeons, and then, being no better, get sent to a psychiatrist who diagnoses a depression or anxiety state. Inter-speciality rivalries also exist which tend to impair communication between the various specialisations. Another source of difficulty in communication between doctors is the hierarchical system within the profession. When a consultant and a junior doctor are doing a ward round together, the junior will answer questions put to him by the chief, but is less likely to volunteer information spontaneously. The relationship is rarely reciprocal, and communication may to that extent be impaired.

Communication Between Nurses

The same applies to communication between nurses. Junior nurses begin their training in hospital wards rather earlier than doctors, and young girls may be more frightened of senior nursing staff than the newly qualified doctor is in awe of his seniors. There is good evidence that some young nurses are sometimes too frightened to mention information to their seniors which it is important they should know. There is less marked specialisation between nurses, but inter-speciality rivalries are not unknown, and these add their share to impaired communication.

Communication Between Doctors and Nurses

There are times when the nurse, just because she sees more of the patient than the doctor, is aware of the patient's mental state, his anxieties and his worries, but is unable to communicate these to the doctor on the patient's behalf. The patient himself is even less able to tell the doctor what he is feeling. All the nurse can do is to smooth the patient's passage through hospital. It is all too often the practice for doctors to discuss the patient at the foot of the bed, or sufficiently in the patient's hearing for him to catch enough of the talk to become alarmed. The nurse may be well aware that the patient is taking in much of the chatter, but may be unable, for professional reasons, to say anything to the doctor. After the ward round is over she can have a talk with the various patients concerned calming their fears and reassuring them. On the other hand, the doctor might want to make quite sensible changes of routine in the ward which he conceives to be to the patients' benefit, but is unable to bring these about because the sister is unable or unwilling to exchange views with the doctor on the matter.

Communication Between the Doctor and Patient

An understanding of the factors involved in communication between the doctor and his patients necessitates some discussion of the effect of medical training on the doctor himself.

A medical training involves not only the learning of a vast amount of factual data and manipulative skills, but it also involves the acquisition of some new emotional habits and responses which are alien to him. First the medical student has to get used to handling dead bodies. Then he has to learn how to make intimate physical examinations of total strangers of both sexes without embarrassment. He has to come to close quarters with death and heartbreak, often in dramatic and emotional circumstances. He has to cope with people in pain and acute discomfort: sometimes caused by his own examination or treatment. He has to come close to, and deal with appalling injuries and disfigurements. He has to learn how to break bad news to distraught relatives. All these things make a great emotional impact, and an untrained person would be unable to cope with such emotional stress. As he proceeds through his long training, the medical student takes evasive action in order to protect himself from the emotional impact of these new experiences. He has to find a way of guarding himself from becoming emotionally involved in it all. One way of doing this is to dehumanise the patient, to forget that he is a person and to treat him as a case. To some extent, of course, this has to be done. It would be intolerable for any doctor to regard all his cases with the same intensity that he might regard a sick relative. On the other hand if he allows the process to go too far, if he grows too thick a professional skin, then he will lose that sympathetic human contact with his patients without which he will never be able to get that full understanding of the case which is so essential to its proper handling. If the process of de-humanisation goes too far, the doctor will make the mistake of talking at the foot of the bed, because he has forgotten what it is like to be there, ill in bed, with only a hazy idea of medical matters, yet knowing enough to be alarmed at the half-heard and partly understood words and phrases that come his way. He may also make the mistake of subjecting the patient to alarming examinations with inadequate preparation and explanation.

When the patient feels the doctor does not understand him, or is more interested in the symptoms or illness than in him, then he may react by responding so poorly to the doctor's questions that the latter never gets a proper medical history, and no proper description of the patient's illness and symptoms. Many patients become acutely anxious if they feel the doctor has not understood them, and the loss of confidence in their doctor may impair their speed of recovery, and may introduce dangers in the course of their treatment which might otherwise be absent.

Patients are, in any case, very variable in the attitudes they adopt to their doctors. Some treat them as demi-gods, others regard them as useless quacks. Some patients are civil and polite, others are unexpectedly rude and aggressive, while some seem unaccountably terrified. These reactions often bear little relation to the attitude the doctor has taken, and may be a reflection, in fact, of the attitude the patient was in the habit of adopting to his own father. This attitude is then transferred to the doctor as the new father-figure. This is a likely explanation, since it is frequently observed that patients regress in hospital, and adopt emotional attitudes to those looking after them, which would be more appropriate to people much younger. If the patient's father was weak and incompetent, the doctor may be seen as such, quite irrespective of the true situation.

Communication Between the Nurse and the Patient

Since the nurse has to cope with the patient for longer periods than the doctor, she is less likely to dehumanise him. She has to be so much more *en rapport* with the patient because she has to persuade him to do what is required of him. The patient is usually not quite so much in awe of the nurse as he is of the doctor, nor does he regard her as such a powerful figure as the doctor. But here again some patients may transfer to the sister attitudes they developed in relation to their own mothers.

Communication Between the Doctor and the Patients' Relatives

Many of the stressful emotional situations which the doctor has to face occur with the patients' relatives, and it is clearly necessary for there to be some degree of professional aloofness on the part of the doctor. But it is none the less important for the doctor to gain and maintain the confidence and trust of the relatives, especially when the patient is a child. Here the doctor has to strike a happy medium between an apparent unfeeling professional aloofness, and a degree of emotional involvement which would become unmanageable or intolerable to himself. Obviously, confidence in the doctor's ability and willingness to help must arise from a belief on the relatives' part that the doctor really cares about the welfare of the patient and fully understands the case.

Communication Between the Doctor and the Medical Auxiliary

Medical auxiliaries exist because they have at their command a professional or technical skill which the doctor does not himself usually possess. They do not merely perform tasks which the doctor could do himself if he had the time. This might have been so in an earlier day, but the specialities of biochemistry, psychology, radiography and biophysics are now so advanced that an ordinary medical training could not hope to make any doctor proficient in these fields as well as his own. He has therefore to appeal to a professional or technical expert for information or skills which he himself cannot supply. In some cases this may cause difficulty as the doctor may feel that the medical auxiliary is something of a threat to him, knows more than he does about some aspects of his patients, and may try to usurp his authority in managing the case. This need never arise if the respective roles have been worked out. The role of the medical auxiliary is to advise the doctor on relevant aspects of the case, never to take the case over. Decisions about the management, treatment and disposal of the patient remain the doctor's responsibility.

Of the various medical auxiliaries, the clinical psychologist is the only one who is likely to have any prolonged contact with the patient. The patient usually casts people he meets in hospital in the role of doctor, nurse or domestic worker. The psychologist is often, therefore, given the role of doctor by the patient. It is often an advantage for the psychologist to try and establish a different or modified role. This is helped if he does not wear a white coat. His approach will be informal: more like the casual visitor than the busy professional. In this way he can establish a distinctive role, and may be able to obtain data about the patient which is new and important, just because the relationship is different.

Communication Between Patients

Patients often confide in one another in a way they fail to do with members of the hospital staff. While they may, with greater or less success, reassure one another, they may equally well alarm one another with grisly hospital stories. Accounts of operations and of instrumental investigations may be greatly exaggerated so that patients expecting to be so operated on or examined may be needlessly alarmed. Patients often interpret benign events in the ward as having some dire significance. If a patient is moved to a bed near the door, some

Jeremiah in the ward is bound to say that this is because the patient is expected to die and that sister wants him near the door so that the corpse can be removed with as little fuss as possible. On the other hand one cheerful extraverted patient may encourage a whole ward into an optimistic frame of mind.

Most doctors become good at communication with their patients and colleagues. A few remain very bad indeed. Doctors who conspicuously fail to make adequate contact with their patients are usually those who have so successfully dehumanised their patients that they are seen merely as interesting cases, exemplifying this or that disorder, or as technical problems, or just as plain nuisances. Doctors who reach an understanding of their patients and their difficulties are those who have managed to halt the drift to dehumanisation at the stage when they can still see a patient both as a case demanding their professional skill, and as a person, with a mind as well as a body, who is asking for their sympathetic understanding.

SELECTED BIBLIOGRAPHY

1. *What's Wrong with Hospitals?* Cohen, G. L. 1964. London: Penguin.
2. *People in Hospital.* Barnes, E. 1961. London: Macmillan.
3. *The Patient's Attitude to Nursing, Care.* McGhie, A. 1961. Edinburgh: Livingstone.

GLOSSARY OF TECHNICAL TERMS

ABREACTION: The process of discharging repressed emotion, usually associated with a forgotten experience, brought about by remembering the experience under the influence of *free-association* (q.v.), *hypnosis* (q.v.) or drugs.

AFFECTION: *Feeling* (q.v.) and *emotion* (q.v.).

AMNESIA: A partial or total inability to recall or recognise past experiences.

ANTEROGRADE AMNESIA: Amnesia for events immediately *following* the shock or trauma causing it (see *post-traumatic amnesia*).

ASTHENIC: A type of human physique characterised by long limbs, poor musclature and little body fat.

ATHLETIC: A type of human physique characterised by broad shoulders, good musclature and by a well-balanced proportion of trunk and limbs.

AUTOCHTHONOUS: A term applied to ideas which occur independently of the train of thought at the time, and foreign to the normal mode of thought.

BEHAVIOURISM: An approach to psychology which emphasises the importance of an objective study of behaviour, rather than a subjective study of personal experience.

CATHARSIS: The same as *abreaction* (q.v.).

CEREBROTONIA: The temperamental pattern said to be shown by people of *ectomorphic* (q.v.) physique, characterised by shyness, restraint, love of privacy, hypersensitivity and love of intellectual pursuits.

CHARACTER: Refers to a person's more or less enduring pattern of conative personality traits: strength of will, tenacity of purpose and persistence in the face of difficulties.

COGNITION: A term referring to all experience and behaviour concerned with, or leading to, knowledge: perceiving, remembering, imagining, thinking, etc.

COMPENSATION: A mental dynamism by which a person covers up an undesirable trait by developing and emphasising a more desirable one. Sometimes applied when a handicapped person overcomes his handicap and becomes more than usually proficient in that very skill.

CONATION: A term referring to all experience and behaviour concerned with willing or striving; impulses, desires, cravings, action and effort of all kinds.

CONDITIONING: A process by which a response comes to be produced by a stimulus other than that to which it is the normal response.

CONFABULATION: Occurs in certain kinds of amnesic states, in which the patient fills in the gaps in his memory with imagined and fabricated events, which he " remembers " as if they had really happened.

CONFLICT: Refers to the opposition between two or more contradictory impulses, wishes, drives or needs. This usually produces unpleasant emotional tension and may lead to repression of one or more of the impulses, etc.

CONSOLIDATION: A term applied to the process whereby a memory in course of time becomes fixed so that it is less vulnerable than it was to loss by concussion, E.C.T. or other cause. This may involve change in cell structure at the molecular level.

CONTROL GROUP: A group of subjects, comparable in all important ways to an experimental group, which receives the same treatment as the experimental group except for those conditions the influence of which it is the purpose of the experiment to discover.

CORRELATION: The tendency of certain paired measures to vary concomitantly. A high correlation approximates to 1.0, a low one to 0.0.

CYCLOTHYMIA: A condition in which a person varies between extremes of mood, from exuberance at one extreme to depression at the other.

DÉJÀ VU: An illusion of *recognition* (q.v.) in which a new experience is incorrectly recognised as having occurred before. The predominant feeling is one of familiarity.

DELUSION: A false belief which is out of keeping with the person's sex, age, upbringing, education and cultural background. It is more or less unshakeable in the face of logical and rational demonstration of its falsity.

DEMENTIA: A permanent deterioration of intellectual functions, accompanied by dilapidated conduct.

DETERMINISM: The working principle according to which all phenomena are considered as necessary consequents of antecedent conditions.

DISORIENTATION: A pathological condition in which a person is uncertain who or where he is, and may not know the time, date, season, year, etc.

DISPLACEMENT: A mental dynamism in which a person transfers an emotional response from one person or object to another; usually because of a conflict situation making it difficult for him to respond in that particular way to the original person or object.

DISSOCIATION: A mental dynamism in which there is a functional interruption between associations normally present in thinking. This may occur in conflict situations and may lead to massive repression of painful memories.

DOUBLE BLIND TRIAL: A drug trial in which neither the patient, nor the doctors and nurses, know whether the drug being administered contains the active agent or whether it is a *placebo* (q.v.).

DRIVE: A stimulus for a particular type of behaviour arising from a physical or psychological *need* (q.v.).

DRIVE EMOTION: An emotion which arises when there is an unsatisfied need. This increases if satisfaction of the need is frustrated and decreases as the need is satisfied. This type of emotion is usually unpleasant; and acts as the tension or drive to behaviour which might lead to satisfaction of the need.

DYSTHYMIA: A term applied by Eysenck to the group of neurotic symptoms observed in unstable introverted people. These include depression, anxiety and obsessional symptoms.

ECTOMORPHY: The component of human physique characterised by marked linearity and fragility, a very large surface area in relation to body weight, and a large central nervous system.

EDUCTION OF CORRELATES: A term used by Spearman for the mental operation whereby an idea and a relation could give rise to a correlative idea, e.g., A foot is larger than *an inch*. " Inch " is the educed correlate.

EDUCTION OF RELATIONS: A term used by Spearman for the mental operation whereby two ideas could give rise to an apprehension of the relation between them, e.g., A foot is *longer* than an inch. " Longer " is the educed relation.

ELECTRO-CONVULSIVE THERAPY: (E.C.T.). One of the physical treatments of psychiatric illness, in which the motor cortex is stimulated by a brief electric current passing between two electrodes placed on the temples. This gives rise to an epileptic fit.

ELECTRO-ENCEPHALOGRAM (E.E.G.). The record of the electrical activity of the brain that physiologists obtain by placing electrodes over the scalp and tracing differences in electric potential between one electrode and another. The sensitive electronic instrument used for this purpose is called an electro-encephalograph.

EMOTION: In this book the term is used to describe the state of tension involving a characteristic feeling accompanied by autonomic changes in the body, which arises either when a need is unsatisfied (*drive emotion*) (q.v.) or when it is being, or has been, satisfied (*reward emotion*) (q.v.).

ENDOMORPHY: The component of human physique characterised by a relative preponderance of soft roundness throughout the various regions of the body, with massive digestive viscera.

ENURESIS: Involuntary discharge of urine, usually during sleep (nocturnal enuresis), but sometimes while the patient is awake (diurnal enuresis).

EXTINCTION: The term applied to the gradual disappearance of a conditioned response in the absence of *reinforcement* (q.v.).

EXTRAVERT: A term first used by Jung to describe a psychological type characterised by an interest in the outer world of practical reality, rather than the inner world of fantasy. Such a person is adaptable to changing circumstances.

FANTASY: A mental dynamism in which a person seeks to enjoy satisfaction of his desires in imagination rather than in reality.

FEELING: An affective experience, especially of pleasantness or unpleasantness which colours cognitive and conative experiences.

FREE-ASSOCIATION: A fundamental method used in *psycho-analysis* (q.v.), in which associations of ideas are allowed to arise spontaneously without conscious restraint.

HALLUCINATION: An experience having the character of perception but without relevant or adequate sensory stimulation.

HEDONISM: The theory that man's actions are determined primarily by the seeking of pleasure or the avoidance of unpleasant experiences.

HYPNAGOGIC STATE: The drowsy state between sleeping and waking, referred to in this book as " twilight sleep ". Strictly speaking " hypnagogic " refers to the state when falling asleep, and " hypnopompic " to the state when waking up. These are, however, difficult to differentiate.

HYPNOSIS: An artificially produced trance-like state, characterised by exaggerated suggestibility, especially to commands from the hypnotist.

HYSTERIA: A term applied to the group of neurotic symptoms usually observed in unstable extraverted people. These include histrionics, simulation or exploitation of organic disorder, inappropriate denial of psychological difficulties and regressive tendencies under stress. These symptoms appear to go some way to solve the patient's problems and his suffering is reduced thereby.

IDENTIFICATION: A mental dynamism in which a person behaves, or imagines himself behaving, as if he were another person with whom he has a strong emotional tie.

ILLUSION: A misinterpretation of sensory stimulation.

IMAGE: A revived sense experience in the absence of actual sensory stimulation.

IMMEDIATE MEMORY: Refers to *primary memory images* (q.v.).

IMPRESSION: Used in this book to refer to the first of three stages of the memory process: the stage when the experience is assimilated.

IMPRINTING: A rapid form of learning present in some young animals and possibly also in human infants. This only occurs for a brief period in the animal's early life.

INSIGHT: Used in this book to refer to a sudden apprehension of meaning without reference to previous experience, as evidenced by a sudden drop in the learning curve.

INSTINCT: Used by some writers to refer to a complex, innate, unlearned pattern of behaviour in response to specific patterns of stimuli.

INTELLECT: Refers to a person's more or less enduring pattern of cognitive traits: intelligence, acquired knowledge, opinions, attitudes, and interests.

INTELLIGENCE: The capacity for relational, constructive thinking directed to the attainment of some end.

INTELLIGENCE QUOTIENT (I.Q.): The ratio of the *mental age* (q.v.) to chronological age expressed as a percentage.

INTROVERT: A term first used by Jung to describe a psychological type characterised by an interest in the inner world of fantasy rather than the outer world of practical reality. Such a person tends to be rigid and inflexible and to conform to absolute standards.

KORSAKOV'S SYNDROME: A condition in which the patient has a massive memory loss for many events occurring after the onset of the illness, and in which he *confabulates* (q.v.) to fill in the amnesic gaps.

LIMBIC SYSTEM: The " visceral brain " which includes the amygdaloid nucleus, hippocampus, fornix, and mammillary bodies. It may also include the hippocampal gyrus, dentate gyrus and cingulate gyrus.

MATERNAL DEPRIVATION: The term which refers to the situation occurring when a young child is separated from his mother for more than a few days. The critical period when such separation may cause the most serious psychological trauma is from the age of six months to three years.

MATURATION: The attainment of a state of physical or mental development without which certain skills could not be acquired. This suggests that certain physical and mental skills cannot be acquired until the individual is mature enough to learn them.

MELANCHOLIA: A form of mental illness the chief component of which is depression.

MENTAL AGE (M.A.): The degree of mental development of an individual measured in terms of the chronological age of the average individual of corresponding mental ability.

MENTAL DYNAMISM: An indirect and usually unconscious manner of gratifying a repressed or frustrated desire, with the object of lessening the tension produced.

MESOMORPHY: The component of human physique characterised by a preponderance of muscle, bone and connective tissue, and a hard heavy body with a rectangular outline.

MOTIVE: A conscious experience or unconscious condition which serves as a factor in determining an individual's behaviour.

NEED: Any factor or condition in the person or his environment which assists to a marked extent in preserving his life and health either mentally or physically or both; or which enables him to develop his full potential.

ORIENTATION: Used in this book to refer to the ability of the person to know who and where he is, and to know the time of day, season, year, etc.

PERCEPT: The thing perceived.

PERCEPTION: The awareness of objects, qualities or relations, which ensues directly upon the stimulation of sense organs.

PERCEPTUAL DEFENCE: A term which refers to the fact that some emotionally toned stimuli are less easily recognised, understood or recalled, than neutrally toned stimuli.

PERSONALITY: The dynamic interaction of a person's physical, intellectual, temperamental and character traits as revealed in his appearance and behaviour, by which he may be distinguished as a unique individual.

PERSONALITY TRAIT: An enduring or often repeated feature of a person's appearance or behaviour, by means of which he may be distinguished from others.

PHOBIA: A pathological dread of some stimulus or situation.

PLACEBO: A pharmacologically inactive substance used as a drug. It is usually regarded by the patient as being an active agent designed to cure or alleviate his symptoms, or to produce some therapeutic change in his condition.

PLACEBO REACTOR: An individual who reacts to a *placebo* (q.v.) as if it were an active drug.

POST-HYPNOTIC SUGGESTION: A suggestion made to a subject whilst in an hypnotic trance, and carried out by him after he has emerged from the hypnotic state. The subject is often unaware that his actions are in response to suggestions made while he was in the trance.

POST-TRAUMATIC AMNESIA: Partial or total *amnesia* (q.v.) for events immediately following physical damage or physiological disturbance of the brain, e.g. amnesia following head injury (see *anterograde amnesia*).

PRIMARY MEMORY IMAGE: The memory of a sensory experience which has only just ceased. This lasts as long as attention is focused on it. When something else is thought about, and then the memory once more brought to mind, the experience is now a *revived memory image* (q.v.).

PROACTIVE INTERFERENCE: Interference in the retention of one lesson by another lesson learned shortly beforehand.

PROJECTION: A mental dynamism in which a person ascribes to other people, thoughts, feelings and desires which he unconsciously entertains himself and of which he usually disapproves.

PROJECTIVE TECHNIQUE: A type of personality test in which a subject is asked to associate ideas with formless or ambiguous stimuli. These may be in the form of inkblots, or pictures, or sentences to be completed, etc.

PSYCHO-ANALYSIS: A dynamic system of psychology originated and developed by Sigmund Freud, which attributes behaviour to repressed factors in the unconscious. A term also used to refer to the method of treatment based on this system.

PSYCHOLOGY: The scientific study of human experience and behaviour. If applied to the study of animals, the term can only refer to the study of behaviour.

PSYCHOPATH: A term referring to a type of behaviour disorder without any mental derangement and with all intellectual functions intact, in which the patient is unable to make lasting personal relationships and appears to have no regard for the rights of other people, nor feeling for them.

PSYCHOSOMATIC: Pertaining to bodily symptoms which arise from, or are significantly influenced by, mental states.

PYKNIC: A type of human physique characterised by a small shoulder girdle, large visceral cavities, small hands and feet and abundance of fat in the neck, trunk and thighs.

RATIONALISATION: A mental dynamism in which ostensible reasons are devised to justify an act or opinion which is actually based on other grounds, although this may not be apparent to the rationaliser.

REACTION FORMATION: A mental dynamism in which a personality trait is developed so as to repress and conceal its antithesis which is disapproved of.

RECALL: The production of a memory image either by deliberate effort, or in association with other *revived memory images* (q.v.).

RECENT MEMORY: The reproduction of memories of experiences which have taken place in the fairly recent past. This includes all *revived memory images* (q.v.) up to three or four months old.

RECOGNITION: The perception or imagery of an object or idea, accompanied by a feeling of familiarity or the conviction that the same object or idea has been experienced before (see *déjà vu*).

REGRESSION: A mental dynamism in which a person, under stress, reverts to an emotional state with concomitant behaviour more appropriate to a younger person.

REINFORCEMENT: Used in this book to refer to the following of a conditioned response, by the unconditioned stimulus.

REMOTE MEMORY: The reproduction of memories of experiences which have taken place at least three or four months previously and which have had time to become thoroughly *consolidated* (q.v.) and which are resistant to loss.

REPRESSION: A mental dynamism whereby painful memories are forced into the *unconscious* (q.v.).

REPRODUCTION: Used in this book to refer to the third of three stages of the memory process: the stage when the original experiences are *recalled* or *recognised* (q.v.).

RETENTION: The process whereby a persisting trace is left behind as an after-effect by any experience forming the basis of learning, memory, habit and skill, and of all development, so far as it is based on experience. Used in this book to refer to the second of three stages of the memory process.

RETICULAR SYSTEM: A mass of neurones and nerve fibres which occupies the central core of the brain stem from the level of the thalamus to the medulla, and communicates with every part of the cerebral cortex (except the visual areas), and with the spinal cord.

RETROACTIVE INTERFERENCE: Interference in the retention of one lesson by another lesson learned shortly afterwards.

RETROGRADE AMNESIA: Amnesia for events immediately *preceding* the shock or trauma causing it.

REVERSIBLE PERSPECTIVE: A type of illusion in which a given picture is seen, or interpreted, successively in two different ways.

REVIVED MEMORY IMAGE: The memory of a sensory experience which is brought to mind either deliberately or in association with other memory changes (see *recall*).

REWARD EMOTION: An emotion which arises when a need has been, or is being, satisfied. This type of emotion is pleasant and rewarding.

ROLE PLAYING: A descriptive term applied to the situation when a person behaves to some extent according to the pattern expected of him in the light of the particular job he is doing at the time.

SAMPLE: A limited number of cases taken out of an entire group or population, either at random, or carefully chosen to contain the same proportion of various constituents as exists in the whole group.

SCHIZOPHRENIA: A type of mental illness characterised by thought disorder, delusions, hallucinations, and often disordered emotional life.

SENSORY DEPRIVATION: A term applied to the situation when a person is either subjected to greatly reduced stimulation of all sorts, or to a constant patterning of all stimulation.

SENSORY THRESHOLD: The level of stimulation at which it is only just perceptible to the subject.

SOMATOTONIA: The temperamental pattern said to be shown by people of *mesomorphic* (q.v.) physique, characterised by a desire for muscular activity, aggressiveness and an energetic love of power.

SOMNAMBULISM: Sleep-walking occurring when a dreamer acts out his dreams.

SUBLIMATION: The mental dynamism whereby energy is deflected from socially undesirable drives (usually sexual or aggressive) to socially desirable alternatives.

SUGGESTIBILITY: The degree to which a person tends to adopt the ideas or opinions of other people.

SYNCRETIC THINKING: A term used by Piaget to describe a type of pragmatic thinking characteristic of young children, in which everything is connected with everything else, but not in terms of adult conceptions of time, space or causality.

TELEOLOGY: The working principle according to which all, or most phenomena are considered as being directed towards some future goal or goals.

TEMPERAMENT: Refers to a person's more or less enduring pattern of affective personality traits: e.g. calmness, exciteability, friendliness, hostility, irritability, etc.

TRANSFERENCE: The development of an emotional attitude on the part of the patient towards his therapist, which can be affectionate or hostile.

TWILIGHT SLEEP: The drowsy state between sleeping and waking.

UNCONSCIOUS: Dynamic mental processes which do not reach consciousness in spite of their effectiveness and intensity, and which cannot easily be brought into conscious experience by any effort of the will or act of memory.

VERBAL CONDITIONING: A term applied to the rewarding of certain verbal responses by approval, and the punishing of others by boredom or disinterest, so that the subject tends to produce those he thinks will be approved of, and inhibits those he thinks will produce boredom.

VISCEROTONIA: The temperamental pattern said to be shown by people of *endomorphic* (q.v.) physique, characterised by love of comfort, eating and social activities associated with relaxation.

INDEX